The Itinerary

A Christian Historical Fiction
of
Jesus in the Wilderness

Anthony Ordille

Although every effort has been made to ensure that this book's personal and professional advice is valuable and appropriate, the author and publisher do not assume and hereby disclaim any liability to any person, business, or organization choosing to employ the guidance offered in this document.

All events are based on real scriptures.

By no means are the conversations and Jesus's thoughts in the stories to be used for teaching purposes, although scripture is referenced in telling the story. Much of this book is a work of fiction with imaginary conversations. Excluding the Preface, Introduction, Intermission, Epilogue, Appendix One and Two, and Backmatter. Therefore, dialogue spoken by, and with Christ, is enhanced to provide fuller context and meaning to the novel's story. Some dialogue may have a modern-day tone. However, Christ's dialogue, although not word for word spiritually, is grounded in Biblical precepts, principles, and truth, and all scripture references are authentic. Any Bible geographical areas or historical records mentioned in the story serve as a backdrop to the characters and their actions.

This book is not intended as a substitute for the medical advice of physicians for fasting. The reader should regularly consult a physician in matters relating to his/her health particularly with respect to any symptoms that may require diagnosis or medical attention when deciding to pursue a fast.

www.anthonyordille.com

Book Layout Copyright 2017 BookDesignTemplates.com
Chapter Three Photo by M K on Unsplash—Altered by Anthony Ordille

ISBN: 979-8-9878004-7-8
ISBN: 979-8-9878004-9-2 (Hardcover)

Biblical Fiction
Religious & Inspirational Fiction
Christian Historical Fiction

Acknowledgments

First and foremost, praises and thanks to God, the Almighty, my Lord, Jesus, and the Holy Spirit, who has granted me countless blessings, knowledge, and opportunity as a writer, in the accomplishment of my first fiction work, as well as my non-fiction work.

I am grateful to the following individuals who, without their contributions and support, this book would not have been published. Robert Reed, Jeff Curtiss, Stan Messinger, David Miller, Kristina Coleman, Marcus Brecheen, Paul Steiber, Alice Mathis, and Brad Brown for their input in helping me with a decision to publish and/or beta-reading.

Finally, I would like to thank the support from all my family, especially my daughter, Renee, and son, Jarred.

CONTENTS

Preface

The author's purpose in compiling this writing was to bring together Scripture facts from the King James Version and New King James Version of the Bible and storytelling culture, shared as a means of entertainment, some education, and cultural preservation, weaving a tapestry of fact and fiction. By no means are the conversation dialogues and thoughts of Jesus as he wandered the wilderness in the stories to be used for teaching purposes. Although Scripture is referenced in telling the story, much of it is fiction. Some of the dialogue may express more of a modern-day tone than typically heard in the first century.

The prologue, introduction, and intermission are written to help bring the story together. Furthermore, at the back of the book, the author has added a summary of Jesus's ministry, and a full-length detailed list of sixty points covering his birth to ascension, specifically his beliefs and thoughts on the journey Jesus may have walked according to the gospels and other resources. You could use it as a commentary for teaching in a Christian setting.

Over the years, many commentaries and books have suggested that some men or groups of men visited Jesus in the wilderness and voiced suggestions for evil. Some even hold that during Jesus' time in the wilderness, the tempter was a member of his own family who followed him into the wilderness to become the voice of evil. As all this is pure imagination and has not the slightest warrant in Scripture, it must be dismissed as untrue statements and fictional.

One of these characters referenced in such commentaries is used in this writing, but not with him speaking evil. Instead, he speaks uplifting and encouraging words.

Jesus' family did not follow him into the wilderness; he went in alone. Neither did any man follow him! As far as the author can see through the Scripture, after Jesus was baptized, he took a path that the Spirit led him down, and no one knew to where Jesus vanished. Only the beasts of the field were there, along with emptiness.

But what do we know about the forty days and forty nights Jesus spent in the wilderness? Nothing much!

The Scriptures in the Gospel of Matthew tell us what happened in the latter part (Matthew 4:1-11):

> *Then Jesus was led up by the Spirit into the wilderness to be tempted by the devil. And when he had fasted forty days and forty nights, afterward, he was hungry. Now when the tempter came to him, he said, "If you are the Son of God, command that these stones become bread."*

> *Then Jesus answered and said, "It is written, 'Man shall not live by bread alone, but by every word that proceeds from the mouth of God.'" Then the devil took him up into the holy city, set him on the pinnacle of the temple, and said to him, "If you are the Son of God, throw yourself down. For it is written: 'He shall give his angels charge over you,' and, 'In their hands, they shall bear you up, lest you dash your foot against a stone.'" Jesus said to him, "It is written again, 'You shall not tempt the Lord your God.'" Again, the devil took him up on an exceedingly high mountain and showed him all the kingdoms of the world and their glory. And he said to him, "All these things I will give you if you will fall down and worship me." Afterward, Jesus said to him, "Away with you, Satan! For it is written, 'You shall worship the Lord your God, and him only you shall serve.'" Then the devil left him, and behold, angels came and ministered to him.*

So, what about the forty days and forty nights?

> **Mark 1:12** – *Immediately the Spirit drove him into the wilderness. And he was there in the wilderness forty days, tempted by Satan, and was with the wild beasts; and the angels ministered to him.*

> **Luke 4:1** – *Then Jesus, being filled with the Holy Spirit, returned from the Jordan and was led by the Spirit into the wilderness, being tempted for forty days by the devil. And in those days, he ate nothing, and afterward, when they had ended, he was hungry.*

The Gospel of John does not mention anything about the forty days and forty nights. He starts his writing with Jesus being the Word and that John the Baptist is the voice in the wilderness preparing the way for someone more significant. John then goes into pointing out the Lamb of God after Jesus comes out of the wilderness (John 1:29-34):

> *The next day, John the Baptist saw Jesus coming toward him, and said, "Behold! The Lamb of God who takes away the sin of the world! This is he of whom I said, 'After me comes a man who is preferred before me, for he was before me.' I did not know him; but that he should be revealed to Israel, therefore I came baptizing with water." And John the Baptist bore witness, saying, "I saw the Spirit descending from heaven like a dove, and he remained upon him. I did not know him, but he who sent me to baptize with water said to me, 'Upon whom you see the Spirit descending, and remaining on him, this is he who baptizes with the Holy Spirit.' And I have seen and testified that this is the Son of God."*

Incidentally, in verse 31, when John said he did not know him, he wasn't saying that he did not know him as a man. It is probable that John and Jesus were acquainted since they were cousins, but John may have not recognized his cousin as being the Messiah until the time of his baptism.

With the variations between the gospel accounts, the author has considered that Jesus entered the wilderness to pray and be ministered to by God. There were moments of temptation by Satan during the forty days with the three recorded temptations on the last day, as mentioned in the Gospel of Matthew.

The author will explore why Jesus was led into the wilderness in the introduction.

The following story conversations are a fictional view of what Jesus may have experienced, and the dialogue spoken by and with Christ is enhanced to provide fuller context and meaning to this book. However, Christ's dialogue, although not word for word spiritually, are grounded in biblical precepts, principles, and truth.

Scriptures from the King James Version and New King James Version Holy Bible are used throughout the story as a backdrop and reference the time Jesus was here on earth and the prophecies spoken before he was born. Most of these same scriptures are used in their authenticity.

Again, these are fictional stories for the purpose of entertaining readers while remaining respectful to God, Jesus, or any Christian belief.

Introduction

Before getting to the fictional story, let's look at some truth that will answer the question of why Jesus was led into the wilderness.

According to Scripture, the short answer is that Jesus went into the wilderness to be tempted by the Devil. But more than likely, there was more to it.

Before answering why Jesus was led into the wilderness, let us examine the first "why." Why forty days?

The number forty (40) is seen several times in the Bible as a period of trial or testing in order to be cleansed, refined, and perfected. It is much like how products are tested, and their flaws corrected to ensure their capability and durability. In Noah's time, it rained forty days and forty nights. In Moses' time, after thinking he could save Israel his way, Moses fled to and lived in Midian for forty years, returning to deliver Israel God's way. Also, after rejecting the idea that the Promised Land was theirs for the taking, Israel wandered in the wilderness for forty years until all those who did not believe died, after which, Israel entered the Promised Land. After Jesus was raised from the dead, he remained on the earth for forty days before ascending to heaven. The number forty has tremendous biblical meaning, and it is appropriate that Jesus would follow the same purpose before starting his ministry.

Baptism! Before understanding why Jesus went into the wilderness, we must understand the significance of the event immediately preceding it. Stepping back to that day, Jesus was baptized, even though he was not required to do penance because he was without sin. Nevertheless, he would eventually take our sins upon him on the cross to atone for them. Therefore, he humbled himself, placed himself on a level with sinners, and obediently subjected himself to be baptized, just as he had submitted before to be circumcised and presented in the temple. By his baptism, he sanctified water and gave it the power of purifying and cleansing the soul of man. In other words, he instituted the Sacrament of Baptism by which we receive remission of our sins under the outward sign of water. He taught us a lesson in humility and obedience and that we, too, may receive remission of our sins under the outward sign of water.

Just after he was baptized by John the Baptist, the Holy Spirit descendent. That does not mean he was filled with the Holy Spirit. Mark 9:1-11 says, "It came to pass in those days that Jesus came from Nazareth of Galilee and was baptized by John in the Jordan. And immediately, coming up from the water, he saw the heavens parting and the Spirit descending upon him like a dove. Then a voice came from heaven, 'You are my beloved Son, in whom I am well pleased.'"

The heavens being opened unto Jesus means he saw spiritually for the first time. Until then, though he was born of the Spirit of God, his only approach to his Father was through the Old Testament Scriptures. He was like any other boy and man who lived back then. He entered the water a physical being, limited by his mind and understanding. Still, he came out as a spiritual being, with the heavens and the spiritual realm opened to him with direct access to his Father, God.

His baptism by John fully represented what happens to us when the Spirit baptizes us.

While on the subject, only Luke 3:22 says that the Holy Spirit took solid, bodily form. The others don't say the Spirit looked like a dove but descended like a dove upon him. It is unclear from these descriptions in the Gospels whether only Jesus saw the heavens open and the Spirit descend. This might have been witnessed by everyone present. Or perhaps it was only perceived by Jesus and John (John 1:32).

Furthermore, the phrase "like a dove" can refer to the visual appearance of the Spirit or how the Spirit descended.

As such, it is unclear that the Holy Spirit looked like a literal dove.

However, the dove is an emblem of purity and harmlessness (Matthew 10:16), and the form of the dove at Jesus' baptism signified that the Spirit with which Jesus was endowed was one of holiness and innocence. The dove appears as a symbol and a tool of God in both the Old and New Testaments.

Now for the second "why!"

The spirit led Jesus into the wilderness. This was not Jesus' idea to go; it was his Father's. The Spirit of God led him, or as Mark expresses it, drove him into the wilderness. But why?

For one thing, it was to fast and pray. When we are called to fast, it is for a time of repentance and prayer to get closer to God. The purpose of fasting should be to take our eyes off the things of this world to focus entirely on God. Fasting is a way to demonstrate to God and ourselves that we are serious about our relationship with him. Fasting helps us gain a new perspective and a renewed reliance upon God.

But if Jesus is the Son of God, why did he have to fast?

Food fasting helps our human spirit develop dominance over our physical appetites. The Scripture for this account of Jesus in the wilderness only mentions that he was hungry at the end of the forty days. That suggests that Jesus only fasted from food. Since water could be scarce in the wilderness, it is likely that Jesus may have gone through some of the days without water. If that is the case, then that would account for a deeper dealing with the flesh.

As we go through the stages of a fast, some changes take effect physically, mentally, and spiritually. Even though Jesus had a connection with his Heavenly Father throughout his youth and young adult years, he had to spend time in a fast to elevate that connection to uncover the purpose, the ministry, and the calling for which he was created as a man.

Even though Jesus is fully God, he was fully man when he was on this earth, and the time in the wilderness was to bring the human man into submission to the spirit. It is believed that the primary purpose for which God used the fast was so Jesus could be tempted as we are tempted. But why? Why did he even go through this? The answer is found in Hebrews 2:17 NIV:

> *For this reason he had to be made like them, fully human in every way, so that he might become a merciful and faithful high priest in service to God, and that he might make atonement for the sins of the people.*

Since he had gone through temptation and suffering, he is able to help us when we are tempted. He has a complete understanding of how we face adversities and is able to fight battles for us.

Therefore, one main reason Jesus was led by the Spirit into the wilderness was to set aside his divine nature to experience our temptations.

But you may ask, was Jesus honestly tempted? After all, James 1:13 says that God cannot be tempted with evil, nor does he himself tempt any man. Yes, that is true; the Bible says that. But yet, the Bible also clearly teaches that Jesus was tempted. We read that in Matthew 4:1-2:

> *Then Jesus was led up by the Spirit into the wilderness to be tempted by the devil. And when he had fasted forty days and forty nights, afterward he was hungry.*

When we read that verse, we can confidently say that Jesus was tempted according to Scripture. But he did not have that inward susceptibility to succumb to the temptation to sin. Because the Bible says a man is tempted when his own desires draw him away and entice him. And for that temptation to work, we have to desire and want the thing offered to us. When the Devil has cooperation from the person he is tempting, that leads to the completion of the temptation, leading to sin.

We know that Jesus was sinless, but that does not mean he was not tempted. He felt the pressure and presence of temptation, giving him a better understanding to complete his work as a man.

Before we move on to the story of the wilderness experience, as it sometimes is called, the author wants to disclose how he knows Jesus was sinless.

When the breath of God formed Adam and Eve, they were sinless until their disobedience in the Garden of Eden. That disobedience brought sin into this world according to Genesis 3:6. And we know that with their sin came death, and humanity is now born with a sinful nature as found in Romans 5:12-19 and is brought on the moment we are conceived as seen in Psalm 51:5. The sin is transferred through the seed of the father.

Since Jesus is through the incorruptible seed of the Holy Spirit, he has no capability to sin.

Not in his deity did he resist, but in his perfect manhood. Manhood is, however, never able to successfully resist the temptations of the devil, save when fulfilling the divine intention of depending upon God and thus being guided by the Spirit of God. Meaning, the Man Jesus was led by the Spirit into the wilderness and was led by the Spirit through the process of temptation.

The Bible in Hebrews 4:15, 2 Corinthians 5:21, and 1 John 3:5 makes it clear that Jesus Christ, though tempted in every way just as we are, never sinned. The apostle Peter clearly says, "He committed no sin, and no deceit was found in his mouth" (1 Peter 2:22).

You may be asking yourself, "I can see that Jesus was tempted, but why?"

In the three gospel accounts, Matthew, Mark, and Luke that refer to the entrance of the wilderness, we have to keep in mind that a divine plan was being worked out. God laid out one before Jesus was formed in Mary's womb. It was not happenstance that Jesus met Satan and was tried. Neither did the devil arrange the temptation.

The temptation here is in the divine plan and purpose. Jesus went into the wilderness under the guidance of the Holy Spirit to find the Devil. The Spirit took him to the place of temptation and was with Jesus every moment of those forty days and nights right through the process of temptation. At no time did his Father ever dessert him or leave him alone. God was always with his son, and Jesus walked, from the time of his baptism by John the Baptist, in the spiritual awareness of his Father's love and delight in him.

It is a popular argument that the enemy drove Christ into a corner and tempted him. But the whole divine story reveals that the facts were quite otherwise. God's perfect Man, led by the Spirit, passes down into the wilderness and compels the adversary to stand out clear from all secondary causes and to enter into direct combat. This is not the Devil's methods. He always puts something between himself and the man he would tempt. He hides his own personality wherever possible.

One of the other things that is possible is that God used it as a transition from man to the priesthood. Indeed, Jesus may have had lots of time alone to pray before the temptation took place. This would make better sense of the time needed rather than the picture of Jesus being tempted for forty days.

God intends prayer to be the means of obtaining his solutions in many situations. We pray in preparation for significant decisions (Luke 6:12-13), to overcome demonic barriers (Matthew 17:14-21), to gather workers for the spiritual harvest (Luke 10:2), to gain strength to overcome temptation (Matthew 26:41), and to obtain the means of strengthening others spiritually (Ephesians 6:18-19).

The ministry of Jesus as the Christ could not begin until Jesus, as God's manifested spiritual Son, had been successfully tested by Satan, so learning to recognize and defeat the

Devil and all his spiritual host of evil spirits. Only after his successful stand against Satan in the wilderness, having manifestly acquired and operated power over the evil one, was he anointed to be and began his earthly ministry as the Christ.

Therefore, Jesus was led into the wilderness by the Spirit of God to have communion with the Father and then have victory over the enemy for all humanity.

Prologue

It was the spring of AD 26, and a child was born to Zechariah and Elizabeth. This child's purpose was not yet known to any around him except his parents. When the little child was in his mother's womb, he heard the voice of Elohim revealing the reason for his existence.

Ooh, what was that? The unborn child thought.

"That, my little child, is the presence of my Son and the reason you will be born. Even though you have not opened your eyes or even know what the world looks like, I wanted you to know this now. When the time is right, you will prepare the way for him to fulfill his purpose as the Messiah, the Savior of the world."

The course for this divine plan was set years prior, beginning with righteousness and obedience of the devout Jewish priest of the Jerusalem temple and his wife. Both walked in all the commandments and ordinances of the Lord. Zechariah was a member of the Abijah clan and a descendant of Aaron, who was the first high priest and the older brother of Moses.

Just after the fourth watch,[1] Zechariah went to the temple to carry out his priestly duties. As part of the Jewish custom, only the priests were allowed to enter the inner chamber of the Holy Place to offer incense to Elohim. By the casting of lots, Zechariah was chosen.

As Zechariah was praying, the angel Gabriel appeared on the right side of the altar, and when Zechariah saw him, he was troubled, and fear fell upon him. But the angel said unto him, "Fear not, Zacharias: for thy prayer is heard; and thy wife Elisabeth shall bear thee a son, and thou shalt call his name John."

---

[1] Fourth watch is 3 AM to 9 AM.

Furthermore, Gabriel said, "And thou shalt have joy and gladness, and many shall rejoice at his birth. For he shall be great in the sight of the Lord and shall drink neither wine nor strong drink; and he shall be filled with the Holy Ghost, even from his mother's womb. And many of the children of Israel shall he turn to the Lord their God. And he shall go before him in the spirit and power of Elias, to turn the hearts of the fathers to the children, and the disobedient to the wisdom of the just; to make ready a people prepared for the Lord."

Zechariah said unto the angel, "Whereby shall I know this? For I am an old man, and my wife well stricken in years."

And the angel answered said unto him, "I am Gabriel, that stand in the presence of God; and am sent to speak unto thee and to shew thee these glad tidings. And behold, thou shalt be dumb, and not able to speak, until the day that these things shall be performed because thou believest not my words, which shall be fulfilled in their season."

After Zechariah returned home, Elizabeth did conceive.[2]

When Elizabeth was in her sixth month, she was visited by her kinswoman Mary. Mary had been told by the angel Gabriel sometime after he appeared to Zechariah that she would give birth to the Savior, Jesus. When Mary greeted Elizabeth, the baby in Elizabeth's womb leaped for joy.

Without hesitation, Mary said, "My soul doth magnify the Lord, And my spirit hath rejoiced in God my Saviour. For he hath regarded the low estate of his handmaiden: for, behold, from henceforth all generations shall call me blessed. For he that is mighty hath done to me great things; and holy is his name. And his mercy is on them that fear him

---

[2] Luke 1:5–25 KJV. Zechariah and Zacharias are the same person in the Bible. In the King James version of the Bible, his name was written Zacharias. Zechariah is the most frequently occurring personal name in the Bible and can be spelled in many ways, including Zachariah and Zacharias.

from generation to generation. He hath shewed strength with his arm; he hath scattered the proud in the imagination of their hearts. He hath put down the mighty from their seats and exalted them of low degree. He hath filled the hungry with good things, and the rich he hath sent empty away. He hath helped his servant Israel, in remembrance of his mercy; As he spake to our fathers, to Abraham, and to his seed forever."[3]

"Oh precious, Mary, please sit down," Elizabeth said as she pulled out a chair. Mary remained with her cousin Elizabeth for the remaining months of her third trimester until she returned to her own house.

When her time came, Elizabeth gave birth to a son. Her neighbors and cousins heard how the Lord had shown great mercy upon her, and they rejoiced with her. Then, on the eighth day, they went to the temple to circumcise the child.

"Zacharias is so hairy, Elizabeth," said one of the neighbors. They called the baby Zacharias, assuming he would be named after his father.

Elizabeth quickly turned and said, "Not so, but he shall be called John."

With deep concern one of her friends said, "There is none of thy kindreds that is called by this name."

But as they were questioning Elizabeth, they made signs to his father how he would have the baby called. Zechariah, the old priest, asked for a writing tablet, and with a piece of wax, wrote, "His name is John."

And they all marveled at his answer. Immediately, Zechariah regained his speech and hearing. Filled with the Holy Spirit, he praised God and prophesied about his son's life.[4]

John was different from all the other boys in the clan, not the average kid in the group. Some thought of him as unique, and even the townspeople tagged him as mysterious. He had nothing to do with the things of this world and the

[3] Luke 1:46–55 KJV.
[4] Luke 1:57–79.

worldly pleasures around him. That could be because John was filled with the Holy Spirit even from his mother's womb. When the other children were running around playing games, John sat around studying the townspeople and the way they lived so he could better understand their needs. However, there were a few times as a young child he allowed himself to have some fun. Since his father was a priest, John would spend time watching his dad from a distance as his father maneuvered through the rituals of the priesthood, especially as he grew older.

Then, the time came when John became an adult and set out to fulfill his calling.[5] Elizabeth, his mother, looked up into her son's eyes and threw her arms around her son's neck. With tears rolling down her face, she gave him a kiss on the cheek. Pushing back, she said, "May Elohim be with you."

As John turned to his father, Zechariah grabbed his sons' broad shoulders and gave him a kiss on each cheek. "*Shālôm*, my son."

As John turned from his parents, Elizabeth stood beside Zechariah, and together they watched their son walk away until he was out of sight. In their hearts, they wondered whether they would ever see him again.

John was devoted to his task and never lost focus on what the Holy Spirit had told him. He knew he was to be the forerunner for the Messiah, and he needed to go to a solitary place in the desert to enter the presence of Elohim for answers. Clothed in a cloak of camel's hair, a leather girdle about his loins, and leather sandals, he journeyed to the deserts of the Judean regions. His diet was the poorest in the land. He ate locusts wherever he could find them and wild honey scrooped out of the hollow part of trees. He never cut his hair and never drank wine. Water was his main source of hydration.[6]

---

[5] Luke 1:80.
[6] Matthew 3:4; Mark 1:6; 2 Kings 1:7-8.

At the age of thirty, after God had finished with all the instructions needed, John headed to the Jordan River with a call to repentance. He was located in southern Transjordan, not far from Judea, in the uninhabited country bordering on Perea, the realm of Herod Antipas.

As a prophet, he proclaimed to all who would hear the need for repentance and rectitude of life. He warned them to turn from wickedness and prepare themselves for the coming of the Messiah. The message John carried was a cry for repentance, a warning that the time was at hand for the people to prepare for the coming of the king. Word of John spread throughout the Judea regions and extended into Samaritan territory.

He baptized many people after they had confessed their sins. But when he saw many of the Pharisees and Sadducees come to his baptism, he said unto them, "O generation of vipers, who hath warned you to flee from the wrath to come? Bring forth, therefore, fruits meet for repentance: And think not to say within yourselves; We have Abraham to our father: for I say unto you, that God is able of these stones to raise up children unto Abraham. And now also the axe is laid unto the root of the trees: therefore, every tree which bringeth not forth good fruit is hewn down, and cast into the fire. I indeed baptize you with water unto repentance. but he that cometh after me is mightier than I, whose shoes I am not worthy to bear: he shall baptize you with the Holy Ghost, and with fire."[7]

John spent six months as a preacher who stood in the tradition of the prophets, preaching and baptizing, and proclaiming the message God laid upon his heart before Jesus appeared in the crowd by the shore of the Jordan River.

---

[7] Matthew 3:7-11 KJV; Mark 1:7; Luke 3:16; John 1:25, 27, 30; Acts 13:25.

Scene 1—Days 1 Through 13

Chapter 1

Jesus's Prayers

The year was AD 27. Jesus set out to walk the three-day journey[8] from Nazareth to attend the Feast of Dedication in Jerusalem. When the festival was over, he walked a day's journey[9] to Bethany beyond the Jordan, where John the Baptist was preaching a baptism of repentance for the remission of sins and baptizing in the Jordan River—about a half day's journey[10] north of the Dead Sea. Many of Judea and the region around Jordan came to John to confess their sins.

As Jesus started to walk into the water, John tried to prevent him, vigorously protesting, saying, "I need to be baptized by thee, and are you coming to me?"[11]

But Jesus replied, "Permit it to be so now; for thus it is fitting for us to fulfill all righteousness."[12]

Then John permitted it and baptized him. After Jesus was baptized, he came up immediately out of the water, and behold, the heavens were opened, and John the Baptist saw the Spirit of God descending as a dove and landing on Jesus, and behold, a voice from heaven said, "This is my beloved Son, in whom I am well-pleased."[13]

Afterward, Jesus hugged his cousin, John, and turned to return to the shore. John the Baptist then said in an

---

[8] About sixty-five miles.
[9] Twenty-two miles.
[10] About six miles.
[11] Matthew 3:14.
[12] Matthew 3:15.
[13] Matthew 3:17.

apologetic voice, "Cousin, that day when Cousin Mary came to see my mother when I was in my mother's womb, I felt the presents of Elohim when she walked in the room.[14] Even though I was not born, it was then that I knew my purpose in this world. As we grew up together, I was unaware that you were the Messiah until now."

Jesus smiled, his teeth shining brightly as he nodded.

John grinned in return. "Remember that time you came to stay at my house for a week, and I fell out of the tree? My arm hurt for days!"

Jesus turned with a radiant smile and said, "Yes, and you cried like a baby."

By this time, they had reached the riverbank, and Jesus heard the Holy Spirit telling him to go into the wilderness. Without hesitation, Jesus took the six-thousand cubit[15] path that would bring him to a place of discomfort for the next forty days, knowing that the environment would be challenging, but he trusted his Father for the reason behind the journey.

Jesus surveyed the scene and began to wander around in the barren region, noting the scant vegetation and dusty, weary land that was smothered by a dry heat. Having nothing but his tunic and the leather sandals on his feet, he hoped the journey would be manageable. He immediately lifted his head toward heaven and started to pray to his Father for guidance.

"Abba Father in heaven, hallowed be your name, your kingdom come, your will be done, on earth as it is in heaven."[16]

Without hesitation, Jesus added, "I know you orchestrated this time for the preparation of my ministry. Please help me continue in this earthly vessel with your divine

---

[14] Luke 1:41.
[15] About two miles.
[16] Luke 11:2-4. Note that Jesus did not need to ask for forgiveness of His own sins. He had no sin.

nature as I set the course to minister to them. Help me pray for the people, leaders, the world itself, and all who are suffering. Please help me know where I should go, the words I should speak, and who should come with me. Please give me the strength to overcome this flesh and fulfill all that is written.

"I confidently approach the throne of grace to receive mercy and grace to help me in my ministry.[17] I praise you, Father, Lord of heaven and earth. Because I am in agreement with you, and you always hear my prayers, let whatever I ask be done on earth as it is in heaven.

Jesus's time had come for him to do the will of his Father. He asked God to glorify his presence on earth and to do the work that was given to him. "Glorify your Son, that your Son also may glorify you, as you have given me authority over all flesh, that I should give eternal life to as many as you have given me. And in this eternal life, they may know you, the only true God, and the Christ whom you have sent. And now, O Father, glorify me with yourself, with the glory I had with you before the world was."[18]

Jesus continued, "Father, in my time here, I have found a split between the Hebrew nation and hatred from the Gentiles. Help me lay the foundation between all humanity so that they may be joined in harmony. I pray that you will continue restoring the land of Israel and that the nation will recognize that this is from your hand, not by their own efforts. I pray they will be reconciled to you through faith in Yeshua as the Messiah."

As Jesus stopped to take a breath, he thought about the hatred he had just prayed about and started to weep. Until now, he hadn't realized how much sadness was in his heart. After some time had passed, Jesus wiped his tears with the back of his hands and fell to his knees.

---

[17] Hebrews: 4:16.
[18] John 17:1-5.

With a shaky voice, Jesus continued praying. "I have seen how they love to pray, standing in the synagogues and on the street corners to be seen by men. I believe you once called them hypocrites and said people like that had received their reward in full. But help me show that when they pray, they go into a room, close the door, and pray to you in secret. Then Father, when you see them, you will reward them, not man. The other thing I have seen is how they babble when praying. Reveal to them that they do not need to be like pagans praying in many words, for you already know what they need before they ask."[19]

Jesus knew that he was not able to reveal the power of his Father without the help of Elohim. Taking a deep breath, he said, "Father, help me communicate to them that you, their God, only give good things because you are loving and that there is no evil in you. You are a giver, not a taker. May they know that Elohim is love, and they were created by love. When they ask you for something in my name, it will be given to them according to your will. When they seek you, they will find you. When they knock on your heart, the door of heaven will be open.[20]

"Help me intercede for the people of all nations, be one of the watchmen to encourage them, and be an example in their own prayer lives with strategic prayer. Help me to teach them to ask, seek, and be persistent in prayer and that Jehovah hears the repentant sinner and rewards them.

As he inhaled sharply to gather his thoughts, Jesus shifted his feet and blurted out, "Abba, help me strengthen the hearts failing them from fear and the expectation of those things which are coming on the earth, for the powers of the heavens will be shaken.[21]

"Please help me, Father, to care for and extend healing for the broken, vulnerable, and needy in Israel who are

---

[19] Matthew 6:5-7.
[20] Matthew 7:7-12.
[21] Matthew 24:29.

struggling and homeless. Help me give aid, sustenance, and wholeness to the forgotten, overlooked, discarded, or misjudged. Please help me to show them that there is only one plan of redemption for all people. I pray for the redemptive plan, both natural and spiritual, that will save our people in honor of your promise to Abraham.[22]

"Father, help them to be prepared for what is to come in and through my ministry and beyond. I pray you will send many workers to join the vast mission of bringing others into your Kingdom. All terror plots are to be exposed and stopped until your will is to be done."

As the sun moved across the sky towards the night, knowing that his Father would be sending him laborers, Jesus prayed for his disciples, "I pray for help manifesting your name to the men you will give me out of the world. They are yours; you will give them to me, and they will keep your word. Please help them know that everything I have is from you. For I will give them the words you provide, and they will receive them and know that I come forth from you, and they will believe that you sent me.[23]

"I pray for them. I do not pray for the world but for those whom you will give me, for they are yours. And all that are mine are yours, and yours are mine, and I am glorified in them. Our concern for their welfare in both the physical and spiritual realms is that the future church's faith would stay strong through them. As I will be with them in the world, I will keep them in your name. But now I come to you, and these things I speak in the world that they may have my joy fulfilled in themselves. I will give them your word, and the world will hate them because they are not of the world, just as I am not of the world. I do not pray that you should take them out of the world, but that you should keep them from the evil one. Sanctify them with your truth. Your word is truth. As you sent me into the world, I will

[22] Genesis 17:1-14.
[23] John 17:6-8.

also send them into it. And for their sakes, I will sanctify myself that they will be made holy, that they will know the truth of God, and that they reflect the glory of God on earth."[24]

As Jesus finished praying for the disciples and all those who would be helping him, night fell, and the moon lit up the desert. Jesus surveyed for a place to rest for the night. He lowered himself to the ground and rested his head against the side of a rock. As soon as he settled in, an Arabian leopard came to guard him while he slept.

• • •

On the next day, with the rising sun, Jesus started day two of this long journey. His body was still transitioning into fasting mode, where the body breaks down glucose to get the energy it needs to function correctly. His heart rate and blood pressure started to lower to help with the process. This caused him to walk a little slower than the day before as his body went into "battery-saving mode."

Soon afterward, Jesus lifted his eyes to heaven and said prayers of blessing upon individuals, including children, over the following hours of being in the wilderness. Jesus prayed that his future church would grow and that many people on all the earth would come to know him through the faithful ministry of all his disciples.

He prayed, "Father, I do not pray for these alone, but also for those who will believe in me through their word. I pray that they all may be one, as you, Father, are in me and I in you. I pray that they also may be one in us so that the world may believe that you sent me. And the glory which you give me I will give them that they may be one just as we are one: I in them, and you in me. May they be made perfect in one so that the world may know that you have sent me and have loved them as you have loved me.[25]

---

[24] John 17:9-19.
[25] John 17:20-23.

"Abba, I desire that they also whom you give me may be with me where I am, that they may behold my glory which you have given me; for you loved me before the foundation of the world. O, righteous Father! The world has not known you, but I have known you, and those who will see that you sent me. And I will declare to them your name, and will declare it, that the love with which you loved me may be in them, and I in them.[26]

With the sun directly overhead, Jesus walked over to a large rock to take advantage of some shade. Lowing himself to the ground, Jesus let his head fall back on the rock and exhaled long and slow. He continued, "Father, I lift up this generation and all the generations to come. Help them understand the law and all the writings both now and in the future and to understand its original context fully. Father, do not allow their personal experiences and bias to affect their efforts to interpret passages objectively.

"Help me, Father, draw all those who labor and are heavily laden so I will give them rest. Help them know that if they take my yoke upon themself and learn from me, for I am gentle and lowly in heart, they will find rest for their souls. To reveal to them that my yoke is easy and my burden is light.[27]

As the day reached the end of the afternoon, Jesus prayed for Jerusalem, "Dear Heavenly Father, you are the Rock and Redeemer of Israel. I pray for the *šālôm* of Jerusalem. I am sad to see the violence and suffering of men, women, and children in all the land. But I pray for justice, your sovereignty, and righteousness, Father. And at the same time, I beg for mercy. I lift up the Pharisees, Sadducees, and all governments for your will to be done in their lives.

"I ask for your Kingdom to come and rule over the land so that your judgments upon Israel do not void your covenant. Shield the nation of Israel, Father. Protect the soldiers

---

[26] John 17:24-26.
[27] Matthew 11:28-30.

and civilians from bloodshed. May your truth and light shine in the darkness. Where there is only hatred, may your love prevail. Help me support those whom you support, Father, and to bless those whom you bless. Bring your salvation to Israel and draw every heart to you. And bring your salvation to the whole earth. Amen.

"Furthermore, even though our creation is disobedient and does not deserve it, as I so said before leaving your side, I lay down my life willing for them. Not as I will, but as you will. This is why I come in the form of a man so they will have the opportunity to return to us. Thank you for your Holy Spirit that will help me through these next weeks and even the years I have left here on earth. Father, may all of this glorify your name! Abba, I thank you for hearing my heart and prayers."

After two days of praying, Jesus still honored the Sabbath with a day of rest on the third day in the wilderness from sunset to sunset. He knew his Heavenly Father had heard all that was said, and he looked forward to seeing the revelation of his Father's power.

During that afternoon, Jesus sat in awe with the Spirit, focusing on the days ahead. He knew that his Father had a plan, and he was looking forward to his ministry. As the powerful sun rose high, Jesus placed his hand over his eyes for comfort.

Through the distorted vision, he noticed something moving closer to him. Just as he blinked to refocus, he heard, "Ah, look at you, Jesus, being a real man. Do you really think God is going to listen to you? You are in my kingdom, Jesus, and everything belongs to me."

Without hesitation, Jesus blurted out, "Father, do not let my heart be drawn to what is evil so that I take part in wicked deeds along with those who are evildoers–"[28]

Before Jesus could finish, he heard, "We'll see about that!" The image vanished.

---

[28] Psalm 141:4.

Chapter 2

Communication With God

After the Sabbath ended, darkness quickly swallowed the daylight. Jesus continued praying and reflecting on home as he found a place to sit—not on his earthly home with Joseph and Mary, but on his heavenly home when he sat next to his Father in all of his glory and wonder. When he enjoyed making plans and talking about all the things they wanted to do with their creation.

Jesus had already started to enter stage two of fasting. This stage usually lasts about five to seven days after ketosis begins. Ketosis is a critical phase of the fast where the body starts to burn stored fat as its primary power source. As the processes of ketosis are carried out inside the body, one might stop feeling hungry and tired.

However, toxic metals and other toxins are safely expelled from the body as fat reserves get used up during ketosis. This cleansing effect may temporarily alter some people's complexion or cause other signs of a healing crisis. Many changes begin to happen at this stage, and one may start to notice changes in their physical appearance and how they feel.

Even though Jesus was God in the flesh, he was fully human and was receptive to being human in every way. Because of his willingness to be human, every part of his body experienced the effect of fasting as he approached day four.

Unlike the first two days when Jesus prayed, this time, God didn't just listen to his Son, he responded to him because he missed the conversations they had once had just as much as Jesus did.

He looked toward heaven and said to his Father, "Father, I remember as we laid out the foundations of the world, we hoped it would not come to this. Lucifer got the best of Adam and Eve.[29] He has proven how much he hates us; it is heartbreaking that people do not realize this truth. We watched the creation grow within its sinful nature only to disappoint us, starting with Cain murdering his brother, Abel.[30]

"After all their wicked ways through a thousand years, we had hoped that starting all over with Noah and his family would be productive because of the divine sovereignty we had with them. We even walked beside him from time to time!"[31]

Jesus took a deep breath. "But unfortunately," he continued, "the sinful nature was carried over through the seed of Noah and his sons. Father, you know what else was upsetting?"

God replied, "What is it, Son?"

"Because of the wickedness of man, not only did you have to destroy them, most of the beasts, creeping things, and birds had to be destroyed in the flood!"[32]

God let out an emphatic sigh.

As Jesus sat there remembering that long-ago time, his soft eyes grew moist with tears of sorrow that rolled down his face. As he used the back of his hand to wipe his eyes, a slight bitterness tried to settle into his heart, but God cried out his name and said, "Jesus, do not lose hope!"

By now, a new day had dawned, and the sun was beating down on his head; he jumped up and yelled, "Father, let your will be done on earth as it is in heaven!"[33]

Jesus started to walk over the tiny rocks on the path toward a mountain, hoping to find some water and shade. By

---

[29] Genesis 1:1-3:24.
[30] Genesis 4:8.
[31] Genesis 6:9-22.
[32] Genesis 7:1-24.
[33] Matthew 6:10.

this time, he began to feel hungry and thirsty,
level started dropping. But Jesus knew he ha
no matter the cost.

As the rocks crunched under his feet, he co
ing with his Father. "Father, remember when
meeting to discuss your plans for creation?"

"Yes, I do, Jesus."

"Why didn't you allow Lucifer to attend?"

"Well, first, I wanted it to be a Father-Son creation. Second, I did not want any of the angels in my plans for the future. Why do you ask?"

"No real reason. Since we are talking about creation, I thought of how troubled Lucifer was back then."

"Well, if you do not mind, I would rather not talk about it."

"Okay, not a problem."

As Jesus gathered his thoughts, he reached down and petted a desert fox. He turned to his right and saw a water spring about twenty-five cubits from where he was standing. Making his way over, he knelt, cupped his hands together, and slurped up some water to drown his thirst. Then Jesus rose his full length to continue the conversation.

"Father, as far back as I can remember as an earthly child, every time I saw a rainbow in the clouds, I remembered the covenant you made with Noah that never again will all flesh be cut off by flood waters. That brought me encouragement for all humanity and helped me bear the burdens of this flesh.[34]

"I still remember sitting by your side after Noah and his family started to grow, and all the generations began to build the nations working together as one group. It put a smile on our faces, and we thought that the reconstruction of the earth was an excellent move. Then, it happened! They thought they could reach us by building a tower into heaven to have a name for themselves and have power like us

---

[34] Genesis 9:13.

_nstead of receiving salvation as a free gift of grace. I could not believe that after all we did for them, they still became self-centered and blind." Jesus turned to sit down with great disgust on his face and a straight back, almost as if he cursed their existence. "This is why we had to confuse their languages so that they could no longer communicate with each other and would scatter from each other across the whole earth."[35]

Jesus crossed his arms as he brought one finger to his mouth, eyebrows raised as he thought, *That sure made it harder for them to communicate with each other.*

"This was when we decided to focus just on one group of people with the hope that they would be the ones to help all the others! Out of all of Noah's sons, we saw that the seed of Shem would be most effective in bringing about this group. Hundreds of years passed, a thousand to be precise before the one called Abram, the son of Terah, who had a pure heart to call our own."

God whispered, "Yes, he did, I still am proud of him for most of how he lived."

"Father, did you see the expression on his face when you told him to leave his country and relatives?

God replied, "Yes I did, it was the first time I ever saw him make that expression."

Jesus then continued, "I thought he was going to be returning to us right there. He turned white as snow and almost stopped breathing. Then, I heard his heart stop just as you told him that you would show him where to go, that he would be a great nation, that he would be blessed, and his name would be famous."[36]

The morning sun had now reached its highest point as Jesus continued to recall memories of his time in heaven. The sun was hot, and the air was unbreathable during this

[35] Genesis 11:1-9.
[36] Genesis 12:1-3.

transition period. But with his Heavenly Father's presence, his focus was not lost.

"Father, even though at the age of seventy-five he did not understand exactly what was going on, he trusted your word and departed for the land of Canaan along with Sarai, his wife, his nephew Lot, other relatives, and all their possessions.[37] I sat at the edge of my seat, watching as they journeyed through the desert."

"Me too!" followed God.

"Sometimes, Father, I do not understand the human race. They were created in our image[38]—yet act like nothing about them has our DNA. Why did Abram tell Sarai to say she was his sister instead of his wife when they reached Egypt?"[39]

God replied, "Well, she was his half-sister from his dad's first wife, Terah."[40]

"Oh yeah."

"But it was still a lie, with deception as its motive," God added. "Furthermore, the main reason was that Abram became obsessed with the fear that the Pharaoh might kill him to seize his beautiful wife Sarai for his harem."[41]

Jesus muttered, "It was an act of selfishness on Abram's part."

"Even as his sister," God continued. "She still joined the Pharaoh's harem, who rewarded Abram handsomely.[42] I could not help but come to Abram's defense, even though he was wrong."

Jesus commented, "Pharaoh quickly trembled at the harshness of your hand and wrathful plagues and returned her to her rightful place to fulfill our plan."[43]

---

[37] Genesis 12:4-5.
[38] Genesis 1:26-27.
[39] Genesis 12:12-13.
[40] Genesis 20:12.
[41] Genesis 12:14-15.
[42] Genesis 12:16.
[43] Genesis 12:18-20.

God sighed in agreement.

Jesus said, "He was so obedient in the beginning, listening to your every word until his wife Sarai convinced him to go to Hagar so she could give him a child.[44] Were you as disappointed as I was?"

God replied, "Sure was!"

Then Jesus went on saying, "Sarai knew she did wrong but wanted to pass the blame on to her husband for following through with it.[45] That is why I appeared to Hagar after Sarai dealt severely with her, forcing her to run away and hide. I felt bad for her for being the victim in a plot to fulfill your word. I remember I had to leave your side to comfort her because she was so sweet and innocent.[46] She was a young maiden just listening to her masters.

Then God told Jesus, "I remember that time; it got lonely up here without you. But then, thirteen years later, I had to visit Abram for myself. Over that time, as we saw how much harm they would do to themselves, he needed reassurance that we were with him. Abram was blameless, wholeheartedly devoted to his family and us. But I had to remind him. I changed his name to Abraham, father of many nations, and his wife Sarai to Sarah, Princess, and mother of many nations.[47]

"That is why I established my covenant between myself and Abraham and his descendants to all their generations.[48] Also, I gave him and his descendants the land in which they were a stranger, all the land of Canaan, as an everlasting possession in hopes that I would be their God forever."[49]

Then Jesus said in amazement, "Of course, he still had a hard time believing that his wife would bear a child at her age."

---

[44] Genesis 16:1-2.
[45] Genesis 16:5.
[46] Genesis 16:6-8.
[47] Genesis 17:1-16.
[48] Genesis 17:19.
[49] Genesis 17:8.

God replied, "Indeed, Abraham fell on his face and laughed, and said in his heart, 'Shall a child be born to a man who is one hundred years old? And shall Sarah, who is ninety years old, bear a child?' And then Abraham said to me, 'Oh, that Ishmael might live before you!'[50]

"Then I said sternly, 'No, Sarah, your wife shall bear you a son, and you shall call his name Isaac; I will establish my covenant with him for an everlasting covenant and with his descendants after him. And as for Ishmael, I have heard you. Behold, I have blessed him and will make him fruitful and will multiply him exceedingly. He shall beget twelve princes, and I will make him a great nation. But I will establish my covenant with Isaac, whom Sarah shall bear to you at this time next year.' Then after I finished talking with him, I returned to my throne."[51]

Jesus jumped up unblinking falling on the back of his heels. "Over the years, we visited him to help him stay on the right path. I remember you once wanted to test and prove him by asking him to offer Isaac as a burnt offering. Isaac was so naive when he asked his father where the lamb for the burnt offering was.[52] He really was an obedient kid."

God added, "Sure was."

Jesus paused for a breath with his mouth curled to the side and said, "I knew you were going to provide a lamb instead of Isaac."

By this time, the blazing sun had already succumbed to the moon, and Jesus looked around at the empty surroundings. Since there was no shelter to bed down, Jesus found a little spot under the cleft of a rock to rest for the remaining hours of the night.

As he closed his eyes, looking back at the hours that had just passed, Jesus felt encouraged that God would be there to guide him through his *wilderness experience.*

[50] Genesis 17:17-18.
[51] Genesis 17:19-22.
[52] Genesis 22:1-7.

It was the middle of the night when Jesus felt an intruding thought at something he felt earlier in the day. "Are you a little bitter, Jesus? It's all right to hate them; they will only cause you trouble and turn their backs on you."

As he opened his eyes, Jesus said, "Give thanks to the Lord, for he is good, for his steadfast love endures forever."[53] Then closed his eyes and fell into a peaceful sleep.

That was the end of day five.

---

[53] Psalm 136:1.

Chapter 3

Communication With God—Part Two

As Jesus opened his eyes, he felt the sun peeking through one lonely cloud to give way to a new day. With a smile as big as life, he jumped up, ran his tongue across his lips, and yelled, "Thank you, Abba Father, for this beautiful day. A day that you have made, and I will rejoice in it."

Jesus brushed off some desert sand critters and started toward a path he had found the day before. Before reaching the trail, he felt some natural urges to eat and drink something to wet his whistle. But he quickly suppressed the urge and immediately started to pray, "Oh, Father, I put this time in your hands and ask you to remove these urges. I lift up to you this earthly vessel for strength and cleansing. I pray for a hedge of protection around my mind."

By this time, the sun started to look like a golden coin in the sky, and beads of sweat began to run down Jesus' face to his dark black beard. Jesus wiped the sweat from his brow, looked down toward the sand as he continued to walk and pray. He occasionally came across a lonely acacia tree that provided shade and a time of rest. But as the sun rolled across the sky, the shade would disappear, and the heat would try to overpower him.

The heat started to induce a negative mood, and irritability tried to settle in. Jesus became exhausted and dehydrated; with a long way to walk in the day's heat, he had hoped for some more shade.

With his head held low, Jesus turned to his right to see a figure of a man standing in the distance. Within a blink of an eye, the man stood a cubit away, facing each other. Jesus stood straight up, his expression uninviting. He whirled on his heels and asked, "Who are—"

Not giving Jesus an opportunity to finish, the man said, pointing upward, "Look, Jesus, there is only one lonely cloud in the sky to protect you from the sun's rays. Has God abandoned you as he did me?"

At that moment, Jesus knew that the man standing face-to-face with him was none other than Lucifer. "First of all, Lucifer, no one abandoned you. That was your choice not to feel wanted."

Turning from Jesus with anger, Lucifer yelled, "God abandoned me, and he is doing the same to you."

Jesus firmly replied as the man-figure disappeared, "God has never abandoned me, and never will."

Just then, Jesus quickly realized that praying would help keep his focus on the purpose God had planned for him. He picked up where he left off the day before, saying, "Abba Father, as I was resting last night, I thought of the time I was twelve years old in Jerusalem at the temple court, sitting among the teachers, listening to them and asking them questions. Father, I know all who heard me were amazed by my intelligence, understanding, and even my answers when they asked me a question.[54] But what did they expect from someone who had studied scripture since I could read? Not to mention I have your seed! The shocked look on their faces was unforgettable. They thought that since I was starting my Bar Mitzvah, I should not have been able to answer some of their questions. I know the Jewish custom says that a twelve-year-old boy becomes old enough to start serving God, but I have been serving you all my life." Then Jesus busted out with a laugh.

By this time, God called down to Jesus with some uplifting words. "Jesus, my Son, I am so proud of you. That time when you were in the temple put the biggest smile on my

[54] Luke 2:41-48.

face. All of the angels and I were yelling and praising your name. That was an unforgettable time for me. We especially enjoyed your reply to Mary and Joseph when they came back for you after they left you behind, 'Why did you seek Me? Did you not know that I must be about My Father's business?'[55] Did you know they were greatly distressed and anxiously looking for you? They cared so much for you, Jesus. Joseph has been greatly rewarded for taking such good care of you. He has to be one of the best stepfathers to date. Wait until you see his crown!"

Jesus looked up with a pleasing smile as he nodded.

"The way you treated your mother and father was outstanding. You were submissive and obedient to them, and your mother treasured all those things in her heart. Not to mention your respect for your brothers and sisters is one that all will remember.

"Jesus, from the moment you were born into humanity, I have been watching you and waiting for this time to come to pass. The next few years are going to be tough, but you will get through it. I will never abandon you. You might not be too pleased with the end, but the Kingdom will be ours again."

Jesus started to weep and longed for his Heavenly Father. He had hoped for a minute that his time on Earth would come to an end so he could go home. But his compassion for humanity soon took over, and after wiping the tears from his face, he continued the conversation, "Father, they were the best parents any child could have. The extent of love for me helped me bear this time on earth immensely. I know they could not fathom the depth of who I am, even with all their knowledge of the Torah. Even your chief messenger, Gabriel, had to convince them. And as for my siblings, sometimes I wanted to...well, I won't go there. But for the most part, they were a great bunch of kids. I am happy they are part of my life."

---

[55] Luke 2:49.

Then God said, "They were difficult at times for sure, but that will all change, and they will become a big part of the future church. James especially!"

As burning skies started to take a toll on Jesus, he made his way to a small cliff in the rocks that had some shade. He looked around at the emptiness, with only an occasional raven flying through the air and a couple of scorpions crawling through the sand.

Right then, Jesus looked through the haze of the heated day and saw three ravens flying in the form of a face as if Elohim was smiling back at him.

He looked back up to the sky and smiled back.

With that smile came relief in his spirit, and he continued talking, "Father, yesterday we were talking about Isaac. I have a question."

"What is that, my Son?"

"When he was old, and his eyes were dim, why did you allow his wife Rebekah to deceive her husband so that Jacob could steal the firstborn's blessing from Esau?"[56]

God unquestionably answered, "Though I certainly disapproved of Rebekah and Jacob's tactics, I had to use them because Esau is a classic example of a despiser of good. Even though Esau earnestly desired the blessing, I rejected him because he did not have the strength of character to handle my purposes. He had already shown that he despised his birthright when he sold it to his brother for a pot of stew, and I knew that he would have eventually shown the same scorn for the blessing."

"Furthermore," continued God, "I needed to make sure we had the right offspring of genealogy to set the course for your arrival."

Jesus just smiled as he sat there listening to his Father. With his legs crossed, he continued to sit under the cliff. Jesus turned and said, "I am sure Jacob knew what his mother was doing was wrong, but since he honored his mother so much, he obeyed her every word."

"Yes, that is why he ran away for all those years," God chimed in. "Even with their conniving ways, I blessed his every step through Laban's deception,[57] to the reuniting with Esau,[58] to the land of Canaan."[59]

Jesus yelled, "I loved it when Esau ran to meet his brother, embraced him, and fell on his neck with a kiss. I wept with them."

God agreed, "Me too!"

After Jacob struggled with God at Peniel, God gave him a new name: Israel, because he had struggled with God and humans and had overcome.[60] As Jacob grew in the blessing, two of his four wives would be stronger than the other two:

---

[56] Genesis 27:1-40.
[57] Genesis 29:15-25.
[58] Genesis 33:4.
[59] Genesis 46:1-7.
[60] Genesis 32:28.

Rachel, for the saving grace of the entire nation of Israel, and, Leah, for the saving grace of the world as a whole.

As God continued to speak, he made mention of how he opened the womb of Rachel, Jacob's favorite wife, and the eleventh son was born, and there was hope.[61] As Joseph grew, the blessing God put on him in the womb flourished, and he became a hard worker, trustworthy, and a faithful servant. He learned how to be a great administrator, even as a prisoner. They needed someone like that to help keep the Israelites alive during the famine.

After God was finished, Jesus said, "Indeed, then he gets to reunite with his brothers just like his dad did with Esau after twenty-two years.[62] That's another time that made me cry. That really did show his character to be able to forgive his brothers after they sold him and then ending up in prison. It is sad that the new Pharaoh after Joseph died, did not know all the good he did for Egypt and put the Israelites into slavery," he added.

God continued, "Then from Leah came Judah.[63] Judah would be the line to rule over Israel after Moses and Aaron set them free from four-hundred years of severe slavery. It took fourteen generations, one thousand years more, from Abraham to a young boy named David, who would be the first righteous king to rule over Israel after the people demanded someone to lead them.[64] It took a split of the kingdom and fourteen generations to another captivity, and then another fourteen generations to finally get to your earthly parents."

"That is not a long period for us, but for them, four thousand years is huge," Jesus muttered.

By this time, things were still quite lively as memories continued to be brought up between the world's Creator

---

[61] Genesis 30:22.
[62] Genesis 45:1-2. The whole story—Genesis 42:1-45:1-9.
[63] Genesis 29:35.
[64] 1 Samuel 8:5-2 Samuel 5:3-4.

and his Son. Day six rolled through day seven and into day eight as God and Jesus continued their conversation. They reviewed the work done throughout the generations.

Disobedience when Israel left Egypt and crossed into the Promise Land through the forty years of wandering around in the wilderness. Setting up the kings of Israel and Judah. The prophets, Joshua and Samuel, and the four major prophets listed in the Bible: Isaiah, Jeremiah, Ezekiel, and Daniel, and the twelve minor prophets, Hosea, Joel, Amos, Obadiah, Jonah, Micah, Nahum, Habakkuk, Zephaniah, Haggai, Zechariah, and Malachi—as well as the judges and priests.

· · ·

By that time, an ocean of stars lit the sky, and Jesus searched for a warm place to rest since the night air could get cool as God continued their dialog. One of the topics they spent some time on was their servant, Job. Job was a wealthy man who was God-fearing. He was subjected to the loss of all he owned, but somehow, he still kept his whole-hearted devotion to Elohim. Even when Job was subjected to personal physical suffering, he maintained his integrity and did not renounce God. All in one day!

Part of their conversation went like this:

God explained, "When the angels presented themselves to me one day, and Lucifer found his way back in front of me, I asked him if he considered the uprightness of Job, that there was none like him on the earth, a blameless and up-right man, one who feared me and shunned evil.

"Lucifer answered by saying, 'Does Job fear God for nothing? Have you not made a hedge around him, around his household, and around all that he has on every side? You have blessed the work of his hands, and his possessions have increased in the land. But now, stretch out your hand and touch all that he has, and he will surely curse you to your face!"[65]

"Lucifer jumped at the opportunity when I told him all that Job had was in his power; only he could not lay a hand on his person."

Jesus looked up, chuckled inwardly at the thought, and said, "I could not believe you allowed him to test Job that way, not to mention that you allowed Lucifer back in heaven in the first place."

Because God did not like to talk about Lucifer, he only answered, "Even with his wife harping at him, I knew Job would come out on top. Because of his obedience, I restored in inverse order what was taken from him, twice as much as he had before. Even his ten children were restored to him.[66] I wanted this to be a testimony that the righteous are not exempt from suffering and suffering is not necessarily a result of sin. His suffering was intended to foreshadow the sufferings of the Jewish people to accept a suffering Messiah. Lastly, I never allow anyone to be tempted above what they are able to bear."

Jesus nodded as he gave out a yawn.

At almost midnight, God turned and said goodnight as Jesus laid his head back on the rock, closed his eyes, and drifted off into a deep, heavy sleep.

That was the end of day eight.

Since Jesus had a full three days of conversation with his Heavenly Father, he took the next day to rest and pray.

---

[65] Job 1:9-11.
[66] Job 42:12-15.

Chapter 4

Homesick

The night sky gave way to God's morning star on day ten of Jesus' preparation for ministry. With a full night's rest, Jesus was already up before the sun met the horizon and was ready to face whatever his Father had in store for him.

Jesus went about the morning, praying to his Father. He felt a peace come over him and noticed he was not as hungry as the days before, having now entered stage three of the fast. But even in this peace, he started to miss his mother, Mary. This was the longest he had ever been apart from her. He wondered what she might be doing.

He sat under the bright clear sky and thought about how his mother had kept herself busy with preparing meals, house chores, children, and taking time for her friends since the death of her husband. Then with a worried look, he muttered, "I hope Joses finished that table for Liberman. He was expecting it on Monday."

Jesus kept thinking about all the times with his mother as she cared for him, taught him, and helped him with his studies—just a few of the many wonderful things she had done for him.

Right then, he looked up and said, "Father, I thank you for your superb choice of all the young women on the planet that could have been used to bring me here; you gave me the best mother any child could ask for. Mary accepted your word and kept hers to you.

"Even knowing who I was and where I came from, my mother reared me with discipline and a love that has helped me grow to be strong, compassionate, caring, and always to tell the truth. She taught me to keep the commandments and follow the law no matter what comes my way. She even helped me to stay focused on the future when I was weary. Even now, I hear her say, 'Patience, Jesus, it will all work out at the right time.'

"Father, I ask that you take care of her for me and bless her with the five crowns of your reward: the Imperishable Crown,[67] the Crown of Rejoicing,[68] the Crown of Righteousness,[69] the Crown of Glory,[70] and the Crown of Life."[71]

By this time, the blazing sun was bearing down on Jesus, driving him to his knees. The sun felt like an enemy trying to snuff him out—in a mockery of a dishonoring attitude that showed low estimation, contempt, and even open hostility.

He was fighting the urge to eat, and Jesus also had to fight off the beating sun. It was only the second week of a long journey, and Jesus wondered if he would make it. As his mother had taught him—keeping his focus on the purpose that had led him to the wilderness would be the wise thing to do.

The morning turned into afternoon, and Jesus found a narrow path between two hills that looked like there might be some water, shelter, and shade. As he slowly walked, he continued praying and thinking about his mother.

He stopped at a small spring to help with the thirst. As he knelt, he moved his head to watch a jackal that was staring at him from far off. Just then, he remembered when he was in the field with his mother and saw such a jackal for the first time as a boy. He had turned to his mother and said, "Look, Mother, at the beautiful dog."

---

[67] 1 Corinthians 9:24-25.
[68] 1 Thessalonians 2:19.
[69] 2 Timothy 4:8.
[70] 1 Peter 5:4.
[71] Revelation 2:10.

Mary had quickly replied, "Jesus, that beautiful dog is called a jackal. It is wild and extremely dangerous. They are clever, and do not like people, and usually live alone in desolate places. Even though they are fascinating creatures, if you ever see one, do not approach it."

As the Son of God, Jesus knew that the jackal would not harm him, but he kept his distance just like his mother had said. With the sight of that jackal and the thought of his mother, Jesus started to reminisce about his childhood. He recalled the time, after completing all of his chores, that he had gone to play with the chickens. As he had entered the doorway, a snake slithered down from the rafter and bit him. He'd run into the house looking for his mother.

There was Jesus, holding his arm and with tears running down his face. Mary heard him crying and dropped the clothes basket to run into the house to see what had happened. As any good mother would do, she grabbed her son and held him in her arms, whispering into his ear, "I am here, Jesus; everything is going to be all right." Mary then pushed back from him and, with her shirt sleeve, wiped his tears off his face before tending to the snake bite.

Jesus was shaken from his memories when he saw an image resembling his mother. He wiped his eyes before taking a second look. Since Jesus had been in the sun all day, he'd started to see mirages.

It was not his mother, just an illusion caused by the desert humidity being so low that not enough water vapor to form clouds. The sun's rays beat down through cloudless skies to bake the land. The ground heated the air so much that the air rose in waves like an ocean. These shimmering waves confused the eye, causing Jesus to see distorted images called mirages.

But Jesus missed his mother so much that his mind started playing tricks, and he thought she was standing before him. Just for a moment, Jesus believed the image was his mother. He ran up to hug her and said, "Mother, I am so glad to see you; I have been missing you. I was thinking of that time you took care of me when I got bitten by the snake. Do you remember it?"

As he went to put his arms around her, she disappeared, and his legs gave out as anguish and loneliness washed over him. He collapsed to his knees, and with tears streaming down his face, he started to call upon his Father, the only one he knew of a certainty would hear him. Laying there motionless, Jesus realized that the image of his mother was his imagination.

Almost without hesitation, Jesus heard a voice from behind a hill say, "Jesus, where's your family now when you need them? They don't care about you, Jesus."

Knowing that the voice had an unfamiliar tone, Jesus jumped up and whirled around to see a woman staring with a wrathful look at him. *Where did she come from?* Jesus thought. Realizing that this was another attempt to distract him from the Spirit, He shouted, "Help me, Father." The woman immediately vanished.

Just at that moment, a soft wind blew from the east, bringing relief from the sun when the sand put a blanket between Jesus and the sky. Jesus covered his head while moving to a rock for protection to wait out the small storm. As he edged his way along the side, his thoughts of his mother and siblings fluttered in.

Jesus recalled when Mary asked him and James to rebuild the firepit. "Jesus, I need you and your brother James to fix the fire pit."

"Yes, Mother, I would love to help. Do you know where James went?" Jesus asked.

"I think he went to clean out the stall."

"James, where are you?" Jesus yelled with a joyful look and thoughts of how they would fix the firepit.

"Over here," James shouted.

"Mother needs us to repair the firepit so she can cook dinner for tonight."

"Do I have to? I am cleaning out the stall. Why can't you do it yourself?"

"Because Mother said that we needed to work together,"

"Oh, all right," James yelled. "I will be right there; just let me finish dumping this load."

By the end of the day, the two had nearly completed their tasks. Even though James was initially hesitant, he knew his brother always did exactly what his parents told him to do. That is why he said to Jesus, "Even if you thought you could take care of it alone, you still would have come looking for me because Mother told you to. That is why they trust you!"

Those memories brought a smile to Jesus as the windstorm ceased. Jesus eased back to his feet and continued walking as the fiery sun kissed goodnight to the evening.

"Father, thank you for the gentle wind; it felt good to have a break from the sun."

"You are welcome, Jesus," replied a voice from the heavens.

"I know this is just the beginning of this experience, but this body wants it to end."

"Just keep pressing in, Jesus; I promise it will improve soon. Once your flesh gets through this part of the fast, I will come down and walk with you."

"Thank you, Father," Jesus whispered.

"I know we can start today, but then you will not have the full experience," God said apologetically.

"It is okay, Father, I trust you whole heartily."

The darkness quickly swallowed up the sun bringing with it a cool breeze, sparking a memory that Jesus had not thought of for many years—a trip to the Mediterranean Sea when his earthly father had to deliver a table to a family who lived in Haifa.

It was Monday morning, and Mary called everyone together to tell them of the trip. Since they would be there, she said they could visit the beach for a swim in the sea.

"Awesome! You are the best," they all yelled.

As they gathered everything together, they almost forgot to put the animals away in the stall. Joseph had to send

Simon back since he was the youngest and could easily catch up with them since they were not far from the yard.

During the early life of Jesus, the Roman Empire, ruled by Caesar Augustus, had expanded throughout the Mediterranean world and even beyond, creating a network of paved roadways and sea routes used for transportation and communication. Roman roads were used by traders, builders, soldiers, and government officials and greatly contributed to the efficiency of the empire's expansion. Because of some of the conflicts with this new growth, traveling had to be done with caution. Joseph knew that traveling with his family could pose a risk, but because he was no threat to the Roman Empire, he felt at peace. Besides, he knew that Elohim was with them.

"I cannot remember the last time I saw the sea," Jude yelled.

Jesus' oldest sister, Rebecca, chimed in, "The last time I went to the beach, I got bit by something." Rebecca was a beautiful young lady with a very competitive spirit. She had a particular way of getting underneath everyone's skin. Jesus loved her no matter how much she tried to irritate him.

"When I get there, I am going to be the first one in the water," Joses muttered. He and Rebecca were always arguing about who was better. Jesus still prayed for him to be a better brother to his sister.

"Will the both of you calm down!" their father said.

"But, Father!"

"No buts about it."

After the day's journey,[72] which took about nine hours because they had to stop to repair the wheel on the cart, they made it to Haifa. On the next morning, everyone woke up excitedly, looking forward to seeing the water.

"Jesus, I can deliver the table alone, so go with your mother and siblings to the beach; I will join you later," Joseph said.

---

[72] About twenty-six miles.

THE ITINERARY · 51

"Yes, sir," Jesus replied as he turned to join the others.

As they approached the beach, Jesus heard Rebecca yell, "The last one down to the beach is a rotten egg." James and Jesus were not the least bit enthused.

As everyone ran toward the beach, challenging one another to see who could get there first, Martha stopped and said, "I do not know how to swim."

Jesus grabbed her hand and walked into the water with her for her first swimming lesson.

"Thank you, Jesus, you are a wonderful big brother," Martha whispered.

Joseph joined them a short time later, and as they were in the water Jesus heard Mary say, "Joseph, Jesus has always been good with the children. We are blessed to be his parents and see the growth in him. When his time comes, there is no doubt that many will listen to him."

After their time at the beach, they gathered their belongings and made their way back to Nazareth before nightfall. The sound of laughter and the happy screams of kids echoed throughout the roadway all the way home.

Shaking away the memories of the beach, Jesus noticed that night had fallen. He wept with compassion for his earthly family and muttered, "Thank you, Abba, Father."

By this time, the darkness was intense, and Jesus made his way to a spot along the edge of a hill to rest for the night. As his eyelids closed and he drifted into his thoughts, Jesus heard a muffled voice say, "Feeling alone, Jesus? Why don't you give up and return home. Your mother is waiting for you!"

Lucifer's words had bounced right off the walls of Jesus's heart and with all the power from deep inside his spirit, Jesus muttered, "Jehovah Jireh."

That was the end of day ten.

As Jesus rose the next day, he made his way to an area of the wilderness that had a spring of water and provided a bit of shade from the fierce sun. When evening came, he honored the Sabbath with prayer and then rested the next night.

Chapter 5
A Special Visitor

It was the beginning of a new day, and the earth's roof was already playing havoc on Jesus's journey. With a clear blue, bright burning sky, the heat continued playing tricks with the world's Savior. He was hungry and weary as the second week in the wilderness came to an end. With his face drawn and tired looking, he felt alone and missed the sight of people. Until now, the only living creature he had seen outside of the Arabian leopard that watched over him as he slept, were some desert sand critters, ravens, scorpions, Nubian ibex, rock hyraxes, and a jackal, and one night in the distance, he heard a hyena.

He was sitting on a rock, thinking of everything that had happened thus far. The conversation with his Heavenly Father about their creation, the memories of his family, and thoughts of what was to come. He slowly rose to stretch to his full height. As Jesus walked and stumbled around, he never saw a wolf running toward him. Just as the wolf leaped in the air, Jesus heard with a clear, sharp voice, "Leave him alone!" When the wolf landed on his feet, he darted off without looking back.

"Jesus, it is your father, Joseph. I looked down and saw you wandering around like you were lost, and I wanted to come to you as I always had when you were a child. I am proud of the man you became and how you cared for your mother, brothers, and sisters after my death."

Jesus wiped his eyes in amazement to ensure it was not a mirage, like what had happened to him a few days earlier.

He reached out his hand and touched Jospeh's shoulder to affirm that he was real.

Joseph then said to soothe his doubt, "Yes, Jesus, it is I."

With tears running down his face, Jesus fell to his knees as he looked up, staring at Joseph. Joseph reached out his hand, pulled Jesus to his bosom, and wrapped his arms around him. After a few minutes, they pulled apart and found a place to sit as Jesus wiped the tears from his eyes with the back of his hand.

"Jesus, your mother and I never told you this, but I remember when your mother told me she was with child. She was much younger than me, and we were in an arranged marriage, so I thought she did not want me. My first response was, how could she be with a child if we had not been together! Obviously, my first question was if she had been with someone else. I wondered if I was not good enough.

"Your mother replied, 'Joseph, how can you ask such a bizarre question? You know I have not left your side for all these months.'

"But how could you be with child?' I asked.

"'Like I already told you, I was doing my chores in the field when an angel named Gabriel appeared. After he calmed me down, he told me I would become pregnant and give birth to a son, and I will name him Jesus. He will be great and called the Son of the Most High. The Lord God will give him the throne of King David, his ancestor. He will rule over the people of Jacob forever, and his kingdom will never end.[73]

"'I asked the angel, "How will this happen since I do not know a man intimately?"'[74]

"'The angel said to me, 'The Holy Spirit will come upon you, and the power of the Highest will overshadow you; therefore, that Holy One who is to be born will be called the

---

[73] Luke 1:27-33.
[74] Luke 1:34.

Son of God. Now indeed, Elizabeth, your relative, has also conceived a son in her old age; and this is now the sixth month for her who was called barren. For with God, nothing will be impossible.'[75]

"'Then I said, "Behold the maidservant of the Lord! Let it be to me according to your word." And the angel departed from me.'[76]

"I still had a hard time believing it since I had never seen or heard anything like this. I was about ready to leave your mother because of the public disgrace when she went to your relative, Elizabeth."

"I am glad you didn't leave her," Jesus whispered.

"However, after I had considered this, an angel of the Lord appeared to me in a dream and said, 'Joseph, son of David, do not be afraid to take to you Mary, your wife, for that which is conceived in her is of the Holy Spirit. And she will bring forth a Son, and you shall call his name Jesus, for he will save His people from their sins.'[77]

"Jesus, all this took place to fulfill what Elohim had said through the prophet Isaiah: 'Therefore the Lord Himself will give you a sign: Behold, the virgin shall conceive and bear a Son, and shall call his name Immanuel.'[78]

"Then, when I woke up, I did what the angel of the Lord had commanded me and took your mother home as my wife. However, because of our customs, I did not consummate our marriage until she gave birth to you."[79]

Jesus was so submissive to his earthly father that he sat there in silence with his undivided attention, listing to every word with only a reply here and there.

"Oh, I remember that night you were born, Jesus," Joesph said as his mouth curled to the side. "We had to take

---

[75] Luke 1:35-37.
[76] Luke 1:38.
[77] Matthew 1:20-21.
[78] Isaiah 7:14.
[79] Matthew 1:24-25.

the three-day[80] walk to Bethlehem to be counted for the census but could not find a room until one gentleman offered us a stall in his barn.[81] Your mother was so brave and beautiful. I fell more in love with her and knew I wanted to spend the rest of my life with her.

"After the Feast of Trumpets, you were born. She had no trouble giving birth to you, unlike some of the women she had helped give birth years later. It was amazing seeing you come into the world, knowing at that very moment that Elohim was now with us. I did not know at first if I should touch you, but your mother reassured me that it was fine to hold you. I cried for almost an hour that Elohim was giving me the assignment to be your earthly father, and the gratitude I felt toward him for having faith in your mother and me was overwhelming.

"Your mother gained strength during the next forty days before we traveled to Jerusalem to present you to Elohim.[82] After you were blessed by Anna, a widowed prophetess who lived in the house of God,[83] we returned to Bethlehem for a short time. Just after Caspar, Melchior, and Balthasar, known as the wise men, visited us with their gifts of gold, incense, and myrrh, we thought about returning to Nazareth when an angel of the Lord appeared to me in a second dream, saying, 'Arise, take the young child and his mother, flee to Egypt, and stay there until I bring you word; for Herod will seek the young child to destroy him.'"[84]

The expression on Jesus's face left his mouth wide open until Joseph stretched out his arm and, without losing a beat on what he was saying, pushed up on the bottom of Jesus' chin with his left hand to close it.

"That is when I knew that, as your earthly father, I would have to protect and keep you safe until the right time for

---

[80] About eighty miles.
[81] Luke 2:1-7.
[82] Luke 2:22-23.
[83] Luke2:36-38.
[84] Matthew 2:13.

you to take your place as the Messiah. Therefore, I did what the angel of the Lord had commanded and made the journey to Egypt. I learned later that Herod inquired of the Magi where he might find you. They apparently had a visit from the same angel telling them of Herod's scheme because they returned to their own countries on another path."[85]

"Were Caspar, Melchior, and Balthasar friendly? I don't remember them," Jesus asked.

"Yes, they were, Jesus. They were excited to see you and were polite the whole time they were with us."

As Joseph continued speaking, they rose to their feet and strolled over to a small spring. Jesus crouched down and cupped some water. As he raised it to his mouth, Joseph said, "Now when Herod died, an angel of the Lord appeared in a dream to me for a third time saying, 'Arise, take the young child and his mother, and go to the land of Israel, for those who sought the young child's life are dead.'[86]

"However, I was afraid to go there because I heard that Archelaus was reigning over Judea instead of his father, Herod. Moreover, being warned by Elohim in a dream for the fourth time, I turned aside into the region of Galilee, and we traveled four days[87] to a city where your mother and I had lived before called Nazareth and dwelt there.[88]

"This is why you were given the nickname 'Jesus of Nazareth.'

"As we settled in and you started to grow, I started to teach you the Torah and the traditions of the Jewish culture, and because of the exposure to a diversity of foreigners from across the Roman world, we had the opportunity to learn to speak and read the three languages: Greek, Hebrew, and Aramaic."

---

[85] Matthew 2:12.
[86] Matthew 2:19-21.
[87] About one hundred and six miles.
[88] Matthew 2:22-23.

"As you probably already know, father, I kept up on all that teaching, knowing how beneficial it will become," Jesus muttered as he shifted his feet.

Joseph's mouth curled to the side as he continued, "Furthermore, because it was customary for sons to be an apprentice in their father's occupation, I taught you all my carpenter skills, and you became a great craftsman. "Do you remember building roof structures, doors, and windows in those mud-brick buildings when my friend in Egypt asked me if I would help him?"

Jesus nodded silently.

Joseph continued, "As time passed, we started being asked to build other wooden structures such as oil mills, furniture, wagons, chariot wheels, and barges, and to build, restore, and preserve boats. I remember we went to Bethsaida, by the Sea of Galilee, to restore that boat for Zebedee. You wanted to hang with his sons and their friends more than help with the boat."

Jesus replied, "Yes, I was interested in their knowledge of fishing. I wanted to hear all that they had to say."

"Jesus, then you asked me if we could make mechanized, wooded water wheels to expand the business. We did a lot together in a few short years."

Jesus smiled. "Yes, I learned a lot from you, father. You were a great teacher, and like I tell everybody, I learned my craftmanship from the best man in Israel."

"Aw, thanks. That is sweet of you. Do you remember that time you hit your thumb for the first time? You gave out the loudest screech. I thought you were going to call it quits. Nevertheless, you dried your tears with your sleeve and returned to the building. That is when I knew you were an overcomer."

Jesus' face expressed his memory of that feeling he had back then as he shifted his feet.

Joseph continued, "How about when we got that big job on the wall, and they needed a group of men to go to the other side and strengthen it up? You jumped up and yelled,

'I will do it.' That is when, my son, I knew you would be a true leader and do whatever was needed to complete a job."

"Father, one thing I was just remembering last night was when we built the table for a family in Haifa, and you allowed the whole family to travel with you so we could go to the beach at the Mediterranean Sea."

"Yes, your brothers and sisters kept fighting with each other."

"Agreed! But not that much. Maybe Rebecca and Joses did most of the arguing."

"Yes, you are right; they were pretty persisting with each other."

"Especially when we had to stop to repair the wheel. I heard Mother in the distance..." Jesus's voice trailed off. "Seriously, you two," Mary chided. "We have a much bigger problem on our hands. Joses, leave your sister alone. Why do you always pick on her? You are to respect women and not poke at them like a bird. Keep your hands to yourself."

"Yes, Mother," Joses said with an apologetic voice.

Jesus came back to himself, smiling. "I do not think he ever touched her again."

Joseph nodded. "I believe you are right, Jesus. I recall when I arrived at the beach, everyone at that point put aside their differences and was laughing and splashing water at each other, having fun. I was so proud of you for teaching Martha how to swim."

"It was my pleasure. I love all my siblings and want the best for them. That is my purpose and why I came, to make everyone's life better and more enjoyable."

"What was it that you said on the way home...? Oh yeah, you said, 'Rebecca, now you know how to swim, you can come fishing with us the next time we go.'"

Jesus laughed. "Did you see how she wrinkled her nose after I said that? It was so cute. We laughed about it for the rest of the way home."

Jesus knew that Rebecca would not go fishing with them because, as a young lady, her role was different from the boys; he just wanted to see her reaction. Since she approached the rightful age to marry, she would spend much of her time preparing herself for her future when she goes to be with her husband. Rebecca's marriage to Asher, son of Eli, was already arranged just like Mary's had been arranged to Joseph. The betrothal, where Joesph and Eli sign a marriage contract called a ketubah—a legally binding document—took place two years before their trip. Asher and Rebecca were not cohabiting, nor had they come together in the marital union since she had not reached the appropriate age of twelve. With only a year left before her twelfth birthday, she spent most of her days preparing and waiting for the time that her husband would be able to bring her back to his camp.

As the time drew near for Joseph to leave, he wanted to express one of the last conversations he had with his wife Mary. "One of the last things your mother and I spoke about was how you earned our confidence and trust from the time you were a toddler. It seemed everything you did was done with grace and adoration to us both…as well as for others. Jesus, you are a hard worker, compassionate, caring, and you love people. The way you interacted with our customers and others is outstanding, and you are an exceptional man. I definitely saw your Heavenly Father in you and loved every moment we had together."

"Thank you, Father. It was easy to do with the parents my Heavenly Father blessed me with. If I had to do it all over again, which I hope not, I would not want anyone else."

Joseph took a step toward Jesus and gave him one last hug before returning to heaven.

But first, he paused and said, "Oh, one last thing, Jesus, then I must go. I wanted to say that I heard every word you spoke when I was buried with my fathers, how I was the best father that any child could have, and your gratitude for me teaching you how to build things, swim, and swing a hammer the right way.

"It was my pleasure to be your earthly father. Even though there were times that your mother and I were concerned about your well-being, you kept your focus on your life and the purpose you left your throne. Now you need to do the same thing, Jesus. Do not give up hope on this world. Remember at all times who you are. The son of God! The Great I Am! With all my love, Dad."

As Joseph disappeared, Jesus stepped back and said, "Love you too, Dad! See you when I return home."

It had seemed for a moment that time stood still with Jesus' special visitor. The moon had already made its way to the highest point of the sky when Jesus said goodbye to his father for the last time. He walked to a large rock and curled up for the night. Before closing his eyes and drifting off into a deep, heavy sleep, he thought, *I better keep that to myself; no one will believe what just happened.*

He knew that if he were to tell anyone about this, they would not believe him. Therefore, he never muttered a word to anyone. Jesus' time with Joseph gave him the strength to continue through the night and the coming days.

That was the end of day thirteen.

Scene 2—Days 14 Through 39

The following scene is taken from the, *60 Footsteps of Jesus,* found in the back of the book.

Chapter 6

Disciples Are Revealed

A s Jesus continued his journey in the wilderness, he faced dehydration, and his body became weaker from the lack of food. Not only did his physical appearance change from not eating, but the sun also dried his hair, eyes, and skin. Along with chapped lips, he had a weather-beaten face that started to bruise and crack. His body started getting little red bumps that caused a rash from all the sweating.

Why didn't the Son of God speak to himself to make all this disappear? After all, he was God, and he had the healing power through the Spirit!

It wasn't because of any physical constraint but because of a moral imperative. Even though Jesus was fully God, he was fully man and wanted to experience everything humanly possible that would help him understand what the ones he came to set free go through in life. He came to do his Father's will and would not be deflected from it.

Everything he experienced from birth are the same things we all experience physically, emotionally, and mentally. When he dries our tears or wraps his arms around us, we know he does so out of love because he too has experienced what we suffer.

As Jesus worked through the last stages of fasting, fatigue, and headaches became a sign that the journey was taking a toll on him. Shelter was needed. Looking around in despair, Jesus refocused and took hold of the situation with the power of prayer, calling to his Heavenly Father.

"Father, I came out here because I knew this was my next step in what you have planned for my ministry. But this body is so weak, and I need your strength to overcome everything in store for me. Help this flesh stand strong and not waver from your power."

Quite suddenly, a loud sound filled the air, and the sky became a silky-smooth cloak that had been thrown over the area Jesus stood in. Jesus heard a deep familiar voice that rattled the rocks around him. He turned and saw his Heavenly Father beside him.

The Father said, "Jesus, get it together, Son. Do you think I would let any harm come to you? I know your vessel is weak, but I will not let it die until the right time and the Scriptures are fulfilled. Am I not Jehovah Jireh, your provider?"

With Jesus on his knees, he looked up and replied, "Yes, sir."

Then God continued, "Since you left my side, I have always been there for you. I am watching, sending different angels to keep you out of harm's way."

Jesus stood tall to greet him and walked with his Heavenly Father.

God said, "Do you think it was just your earthly parents who reared you? No. I was there beside them with directions and ensuring you would make it to your thirtieth birthday. I need you to know that you will make it through this, no matter how bad it looks.

"I am building you up for some great things that will be done over the next three-plus years. The time has come for me to show you what you will do and to tell you of those who will help restore our people. Even though some will persecute you, many will follow you, Jesus. They will not understand at first, but as time goes on and they see the many miracles you perform, they will believe again."

Jesus replied, "Thank you, Father, for being here for me. This is harder than I imagined. Sometimes, I am unsure if I will make it, but you have helped me regain my purpose.

And thank you for blocking out the sun; it was starting to get to me."

After God comforted his Son, he said, "Incidentally, did you like your special visitor yesterday?"

Jesus replied with the biggest smile, "Yes, Father, thank you!"

"Jesus, Lucifer has been taunting you these last couple of weeks to test your weaknesses. But in a few weeks, he will try to get you to sin. You were not led here, Jesus, to see if you would sin but to prove that you cannot sin. But he will test you anyway. And no matter what he says, being tempted is not a sin. The sin lies in yielding to temptation.

"This part of your ministry is to show future believers that testing is inevitable for the believer. The closer one follows you, the more intense they will be. Lucifer, known to them as Satan, does not waste his time on ordinary Christians, but opens his full power on those who are winning territory in the spiritual warfare."

Jesus nodded slowly.

"Furthermore," continued God, "when you are done here in the wilderness, your ministry will begin by going to Galilee. You will proclaim good news to the poor, freedom for the prisoners, recovery of sight for the blind, set the oppressed free, and proclaim the year of the Lord's favor all over the Galilean and Judean territory. But only after you go to Cana of Galilee for a wedding.

"Now I want to tell you about the men who will be part of your ministry. Later, I will give you your itinerary for the ministry itself. When you leave this place, you will return to the area where John baptized you; he is still there baptizing all who repent. You will meet two men named Andrew and John who will follow you asking questions. Spend the day with them and answer all their questions. Andrew already believes in his heart that you are the true Messiah they have all been waiting for. Spending the day with him will affirm that belief.

"He will be the first to bring someone to you—his brother. He will tell his brother Simon as soon as he leaves you. Simon will become a believer because of their love for each other and trust in one another. Andrew's faith in you will grow to the point that he will know that you intend to save all the world and will be one of the first to be involved in an evangelical effort that will extend beyond the Jewish people.

"John will spread our word and will be accountable for writing most of what you will be doing and will write more that I will personally show him. His demeanor will reflect a passion for the truth, compassion for people, and a steadfast desire to serve and represent us with humility and grace. He will be the one you will entrust the care of your mother to just before you come home."[89] Jesus broke in with a clear, sharp voice, "Thank you, Father! The human part of me is happy that she will be taken care of when my time has come!"

God continued, "Now when you meet Simon, I want you to change his name to Peter[90] because he will be the one we will use to build our church.[91] He is a little outspoken, ardent, enthusiastic, strong-willed, impulsive, and sometimes brash. It would be best to mold him into what you need him to be, even though he sometimes questions you.

"Then there is Philip! He is another of your cousin John's disciples who will join you.[92] You will find him by the Sea of Galilee in Bethsaida. He will be a liaison between you and the Greeks. He will then bring Nathanael to you, who is

---

[89] John 19:25-27.
[90] Mark 3:16; Luke 6:14.
[91] Matthew 16:18.
[92] Philip the Apostle should not be confused with Philip the Evangelist, who was appointed with Stephen and five others to oversee charitable distributions (Acts 6:5).

from Cana. Philip will become a missionary in Phrygia, and many will learn from him."[93]

"What about Nathanael?" Jesus asked.

"Nathanael is also known as Bartholomew.[94] Even though, at first, he will be skeptical to believe that nothing good can come from Nazareth, he will be one of the first to express belief in you as the Son of God. Because the Holy Spirit will fully control your natural man, you can see things and know men's thoughts as if you were sitting on your throne. You will have a vision of Nathanael that will help make him a believer.

"When you meet him, I want you to say, 'Behold, an Israelite indeed, in whom is no deceit!'[95] This will cause him to accept your invitation to follow you. Then say to him, 'Before Philip called you, when you were under the fig tree, I saw you.'[96] This will immediately cause him to recognize you as the Christ, and he will call you, 'Rabbi, You are the Son of God! You are the King of Israel!'"[97]

Jesus replied, "Yes, Sir."

God then gave Jesus one more highlight about Nathanael. "Because you will say those things to Nathanael, he will be amazed at what you reveal to him. Please respond to him, 'Because I said to you, 'I saw you under the fig tree,' do you believe? You will see greater things than these. Most assuredly, I say to you, hereafter you shall see heaven open, and the angels of God ascending and descending upon the Son of Man.'[98] Meaning that you, Jesus, will be the final, efficacious connection between me and humanity.

"Afterward, when you get to Capernaum after the wedding, you will find Andrew and John on the shore of the Sea

[93] "Acts of Philip – especially Book 8". meta-religion.com. Retrieved 14 March 2007.
[94] Luke 6:14; John 1:45.
[95] John 1:47.
[96] John 1:48.
[97] John 1:49.
[98] John 1:50-51.

of Galilee, returning from fishing with their brothers Simon and James. Please invite them to follow you to be your disciples. They will temporarily drop everything they have because they believe in you. You will make them fishers of men!"[99]

Jesus asked, "How many men will become my disciples?"

God replied, "You will have many that will follow you and be considered a disciple, but only twelve men will be students and begin building the church afterward. I will, however, have to replace one of them because he will be deceived. I will explain more about this later."

Jesus replied, "I am listening, Father."

"The disciples will be known as apostles because I will commission them and send them out into the world in your place after you return to me. Actually, there will be a total of seventy-two apostles[100] that will be birthed from your ministry. A few of them will be known: Barnabas, Andronicus, Junia, Silas, Timothy, Apollos, and your brother James.

"Furthermore, Peter, James, and John will become your inner circle of friends and students. They will be eyewitnesses to everything you do and be great leaders within the church. I trust them as much as I trusted Abraham, Isaac, Jacob, Moses, Noah, and many others. You will not be disappointed, Jesus, even when they seem not to understand you. This bond of friendship between the four of you will be rare.

"Especially Peter! Towards the end of your earthly walk, he will deny knowing you out of fear of being harmed.[101] But he will soon realize his role and become a great man of God."

As God continued speaking, the glowing sun rays started to retract from behind the silky-smooth cloak thrown over

---

[99] Matthew 4:19.
[100] Luke 10:1.
[101] Matthew 26:69-75.

Jesus's sitting area. Jesus then released a sound of relief as he listened to his Father's voice.

"Your faithful ministry will begin after you have called Peter, Andrew, James, John, Philip, and Nathanael. You will start by going to Jerusalem for Passover.

"When you return to Capernaum, many people will hear about you. They will gather in large numbers to listen to you and witness you casting out demons and healing people. Jesus, make sure you take some time alone to be refreshed in the Spirit when you start to feel the power leave you. This time here in the wilderness with me will not carry you through your entire ministry. It is imperative that you rest and rejuvenate your spirit."

"Yes, Father, I will remember to do that," Jesus muttered.

"When you are in Capernaum, you will find a tax collector named Matthew, the son of Alphaeus. Some call him Levi, but we will refer to him as Matthew.[102] I know he is viewed as dishonest, but he has an incredible heart. I will use him to pen a famous gospel that many will learn from through all the generations. Matthew is unique, and many will make fun of him, but he will be loyal to you and record your every move. To set the stage and to show certain priests the error of their thinking, you will have dinner at his house along with many others.[103]

"Number eight on your team will be Thomas, also called Didymus.[104] Thomas will be deeply committed to you as his master, yet he will struggle with doubts and questions. After your resurrection, when you appear to some of the disciples, they will tell him they have seen the resurrected Lord. He will reply to them, 'Unless I see the nail marks in his hands, put my finger where the nails were, and put my hand into

---

[102] Mark 2:14.
[103] Mark 2:15.
[104] John 11:16 NIV.

his side; I will not believe.'[105] Therefore Jesus, when you appear to them again, you will have to let Thomas touch you.

"Jesus, as you continue throughout the land of Galilee, you will meet James, the son of Alphaeus—who is sometimes known as Clopas.[106] James will not be known for much as some of the others, but he will be known for his faithfulness, endurance, obedience, and sacrifice. He will be instrumental in laying out the foundation of your message."

"I trust that all who are called by you, Father, will play their part in this final journey you have me on," Jesus said.

"Yes, they will, Jesus," God replied. "Furthermore, following James will be Judas, also known as Thaddeus.[107] Judas is a gentle soul with a tender, childlike heart. He will work hard for you and listen to your every word. He will keep an account of some of the work you do and write a book that will be titled after his name. Furthermore, James is expecting a Messiah who will reveal himself in power to the world, so when you return to them after your resurrection, he will question you.

"Because of the diversity of men joining you, I want to add someone in the political world to help reveal how the power of God can change a person: Simon the Zealot.[108] He will listen to everything you say and watch your every move. Then we will use him to preach the gospel to Persia. Sadly though, because of his faithfulness to us, he will be killed for refusing to sacrifice to the sun god."[109]

---

[105] John 20:25.

[106] This name, Clopas, is thought by many to be the Greek transliteration of an Aramaic Alphaeus.

[107] John 14:22, Luke 6:16, and Acts 1:13 say Judas, and Matthew 10:3 and Mark 3:18 say Thaddeus.

[108] It is usually assumed that he is called "Simon the Zealot" because, when Jesus called him, he was a member of the Zealots' political movement.

[109] Tradition says that Simon the Zealot preached the gospel in Persia and was ultimately killed for refusing to sacrifice to the sun god.

At this point, God turned and said, "Jesus, I know you are tired and would like to rest. We only have three more men to talk about, and then you will be able to rest for the night."

Jesus replied, "Father, I am getting every word you say. I am fine now that the amber sky lets me know the sun is going down."

With excitement in his voice, God brought up Judas Iscariot. "Jesus, the last prominent disciple I want to tell you about has a sad ending. His name is Judas Iscariot. I want you to make him the treasurer. Even though others would be better at it, I want them focused on other things. Judas will be under your teaching but will need to receive the truth. He will remain unclean because he is a thief, and money is more important to him.[110] He will help fulfill the prophecy spoken by Zechariah, the prophet.[111] This is the sad part I mentioned. When you sit with your disciples at Passover (Last Supper) and as soon as you hand him the bread that will represent your broken body, Satan will enter him.[112] Then he will go to the chief priests and the elders to discuss how he might betray you. He will agree on thirty pieces of silver to hand you over to them.[113] Then the next day, they will come looking to arrest you, and Judas will betray you by greeting you with a kiss.[114]

"After he does this atrocious act, Judas will be seized with remorse and return the thirty silver coins to the chief priests and the elders. Even though he has remorse and returns the money, it will not be a form of repentance. Instead of making amends with you or seeking your forgiveness, he will hang himself and not enter the Kingdom of Heaven."[115]

---

[110] John 12:6.
[111] Zechariah 11:12-13.
[112] John 13:27.
[113] Matthew 26:13-15.
[114] Luke 22:47-48.
[115] Matthew 27:3-5.

As God finished speaking those words, a tear ran down Jesus's cheek.

God continued, "After you ascend back to Heaven, we will replace Judas with Matthias to fulfill the Scriptures.[116] He will be a faithful follower of your work, starting with the teachings of John the Baptist.

"Excluding Judas Iscariot, this mutual devotion and admiration for the Good News will light a fire that will survive as long as life itself. They will not only continue to believe in you, but they will spend the rest of their lives telling others about Jesus. They will take every command you said seriously and will "Go into all the world and preach the gospel to all creation."[117] They will believe, beyond all doubt, that Jesus Christ was the Son of God sent from Heaven to save all humanity from their sins.

"John will be the only one who will die from a natural death. The rest will be martyred in horrific accounts. Our blessing is that they are willing to die for their faith in us."

Jesus fell to his knees and wept as he said, "Father, do they have to all die that way?"

"Yes, Jesus, they will," God replied with a sympathetic tone. "Jesus, now that you know who will be by your side during the last days on earth as a man, I would like to talk to you about two more important men. The first one is your brother James. He will be a great leader and shepherd a church in Jerusalem. He will become a well-known author along with your brother Jude. They, as well as Joses, Simon, and your sisters, will follow you from a distance from time to time, for they will find it hard to believe in you because they think they know you, so they will tease and test you. But, after the resurrection, they will believe. Of course, your mother, Mary, already believes in you and will participate in your ministry. She will not be left alone when you return home to me. However, James will be thrown off a temple

---

[116] Acts 1:24-26.
[117] Mark 16:15.

when he refuses to deny his faith in you, survive, and then be beaten to death with a club."[118]

Jesus wept for his brother.

God gave him some time to mourn before he continued,

"Jesus, there is one other apostle I would like to mention. Saul, whom I will change his name to Paul.[119] He will spread the gospel to the Gentiles throughout the Mediterranean. You will meet him after your resurrection. During one of your trips to Jerusalem, he will be in the crowd listening to your teachings. Here is a portion of Saul's story; I will go into more detail later.

"Saul is proud of his Jewish heritage and lives by the law, so much so that he will be zealous and devout to the point of persecuting Christians to show his devotion. His opposition to the name of Jesus of Nazareth will be a raging fury,[120] breathing threats and murder against the disciples of the Lord. His hatred will increase with time for you and all associated with you.

"At the appropriate time, Saul will ask the high priest of the temple of Jerusalem for a letter giving him authority to arrest any who belong to 'the Way,' meaning those who follow Christ. But while on the roadway to Damascus, you will leave your throne once again to meet him, asking in a voice only he will understand, 'Why are you persecuting me?' Others will see the light of your entrance but will not hear the voice. He will recognize the power in your voice but when you identify yourself, his heart will be converted. That will be when we will change his name to Paul to be one of the top apostles building the church.[121]

By this time, an ocean of stars filled the sky, and Jesus glanced toward the moon and said good night to his

---

[118] Although there is no Biblical record, according to the first-century historian, Josephus, second-century historian, Heqesippus, Apocalypse of James, & Ecclesiastical History, 1995, pp. 75-76.
[119] Acts 13:9.
[120] Acts 26:9.
[121] Acts 9:1-9.

Heavenly Father. The air became cool and crisp, setting the tone for a good night's rest.

That was the end of day fourteen.

Chapter 7

Jesus and the Holy Spirit

As Jesus entered stage four of fasting, a daily balance started to set in. Stage four is the extension and completion of the healing and cleansing processes that began during the earlier stages. The longer the fast, the more time and opportunity his body was given to heal and cleanse itself.

Even though Jesus had not eaten anything in days, he felt stronger than he felt at the beginning of this journey as his body became acclimated to change. The transformation into the full anointing took over, and Jesus no longer felt weak. Now that he had overcame the flesh, the Holy Spirit was able to maneuver in the full power of God.

Through the centuries, the power of God manifested itself on earth through his Spirit, starting with the creation of the spoken word.[122] Through the breath of God, he breathed into Adam's nostrils bringing forth mankind.[123] Elohim made an appearance as a pillar of the cloud and fire[124] which went before the Israelites while they were in the desert and in the mountain before Moses. Sometimes, the power moved through the wind as an invisible, mysterious, and powerful force.[125] wherein addition, Elohim said he'd dwell in a certain place, such as the tabernacle or in Jerusalem.[126]

---

[122] Genesis 1:1-25.

[123] Genesis 1:26-28.

[124] Numbers 14:14.

[125] Genesis 8:1; Exodus 10:13, 19, 21; Numbers 11:31.

[126] Exodus 25:8, 29:45-46.

The Holy Spirit is invisible.[127] His power is equal and the reflection of Elohim himself, who reveals himself as the light of the world—strong in nature and everlasting.[128] His existence will never end since he is immortal and infinite.[129]

The power of God even came through men and women that upheld a certain level of trust with God: Adam and Eve, Noah, Abraham, Moses, Isaac, Jacob, Joseph, Saul, David, Solomon, Elijah, Elisha, Aaron, Joshua, Samson, Samuel, Jezebel, Esther, and others. From the beginning of creation, the Holy Spirit never indwelled a person continuously until now.

Jesus knew who he was because of the statement he made in the temple when he stood with the priests and other leaders at twelve years of age. He did not come knowing everything.[130] In fact, he came as a human baby who had to grow physically and intellectually. As a human man, Jesus had to enter the wilderness to draw closer to his Father so that the power of the Holy Spirit could flourish. That is why Jesus said when he entered the wilderness, "Please help me know where I should go, the words I should speak, and who should come with me. Please give me the strength to overcome this flesh and fulfill all that is written."

However, Jesus was not the only one with the power manifested at the same time as himself. John the Baptist was filled with the Holy Spirit at his birth and even in his mother's womb. John, too, had to enter the wilderness to draw closer to Elohim for the power to work through him years before the start of his ministry. Since Jesus was of a higher rank than John,[131] Jesus too was filled with the Holy Spirit at his birth and even in his mother's womb, but the Spirit only guided him through his life as a boy. However, as a man, he was set apart until his rightful time.

---

[127] John 1:18, 4:24.
[128] Isaiah 60:19; James 1:17.
[129] Deuteronomy 33:27; Psalm 90:2; 1 Timothy 1:17.
[130] Matthew 24:36.
[131] John 1:30.

Therefore, Jesus being conceived by the Holy Spirit was the special creative power of God that brought him into the world through a virgin. By entering the wilderness and laying down his will through prayer and seeking the will of his Father, a connection was opened between God the Father and the Son. Through this connection, he was empowered to perform miracles and teach with the authority that Jesus would need to carry out all that was preplanned by his Father, being filled with wisdom and revelation.

This is why God not only sent the Holy Spirit, but he also entered the wilderness himself to give his son words of encouragement, strength, and reassurance that Jesus was not alone.

At times this was not an easy task. But because as Jesus went through this time of laying down the flesh, it not only opened the connection to the Spirit but it also brought temptations. The temptations were used as a distraction to try to get Jesus to sin and turn away from the truth. Lucifer didn't know the plans for Jesus' future but figured out that something was unfolding and felt he needed to put a stop to it. What he failed to accept was that when there was a ramlocking conflict between the power of the enemy and the power of God, the power of the enemy lost every time.

As the days unfolded, Jesus became stronger in this power even as the flesh, through this time of prayer and fasting, bowed to the Spirit of God.

It is with this power and the open connection he had with his Father that Jesus would be able to conquer sin, death, and the grave, freeing mankind from the power of the evil one. Through this power, Jesus was given all authority to conquer demons, heal the sick, forgive those who did him wrong, and teach the truth from God's Law to free people from oppression, sickness, guilt, and sin. No other man was given all authority to manifest this power.

Both Jesus and John the Baptist depended on the empowerment of the Holy Spirit for their ministry. But what does the power of the Holy Spirit look like? How was all this power going to work for John the Baptist and, more importantly, for Jesus?

For John, he carried on the mantle of ministry that Elijah had left on the earth, ultimately turning fathers and sons back to the ways of the Lord. He spoke the truth through the Spirit and prepared the way for the Messiah.

As Jesus went about his time in the wilderness, he gained every attribute of Elohim—character, perfection, holiness, power, love—to walk in the complete nature of his Heavenly Father. It was everything that was needed to fulfill his ministry, as well as a reminder of the greatness of His Heavenly Father and the power of his majesty.

Jesus was not capable of walking his final years to complete the mission on his own accord. Even though he was God in the flesh, he was still a man who needed his Heavenly Father through the indwelling of the Holy Spirit. That is why he said, "Most assuredly, I say to you, the Son can do nothing of himself, but what he sees the Father do; for whatever he does, the Son also does in like manner.[132] For I have not spoken on my own authority; but the Father who sent me gave me a command, what I should say and what I should speak."[133] Jesus didn't have a spirit of independence, rebellion, or disobedience. He had a spirit of submission to the Father.

As the desert sun faded into the night, Jesus reflected on the Spirit of God and everything that he is. He is reliable and trustworthy,[134] unchangeable, inscrutable, unfathomable, and just.[135] He is no respecter of persons who shows favoritism.[136] He is omnipotent[137] and omnipresent,[138] being

---

[132] John 5:19.
[133] John 12:49.
[134] Malachi 3:6; Numbers 23:19; Psalm 102:26-27.
[135] Isaiah 40:28; Psalm 145:3; Romans 11:33-34
[136] Deuteronomy 32:4; Psalm 18:30.
[137] Revelations 19:6; Jeremiah 32:17, 27.
[138] Psalm 139:7-13; Jeremiah 23:23.

omniscient—knowing the past, present, and future.[139] Most importantly, he is righteous, sovereign, and all supreme,[140] and will remain incorruptible and cannot lie.[141] For he is gracious with goodness, kindness, mercy, and love.[142]

• • •

The moon had long since set. Dawn was scarcely an hour away when Jesus rose to greet a new day. He recalled all that the Father had said in the days before.

The rocks crunched under his feet as he made his way between two hills; his olive-brown skin glistened in the sunlight. With his flesh feeling stronger and excitement in his spirit, Jesus started to sing melodies from the Psalms of David. Just then, he heard an echo that made him cease.

A voice said, "Why don't you leave, Jesus? You are not happy. Did the Spirit really tell you to come here? God won't care! If you stay, Jesus, I will do the same thing I did to Job. Don't you love your family?"

Without hesitation and with a curled mouth, Jesus answered, "I am not afraid of you, Lucifer. You can only do what my Father permits; go from here." Then Jesus returned to his singing.

Once more, the sky became a silky-smooth cloak that had been thrown over the area Jesus stood. Jesus heard a deep familiar voice that rattled the rocks around him for a second time and saw his Heavenly Father beside him.

"Jesus, during the next few weeks, I will review your ministry."

"I am listening, Father." Jesus turned his head towards his Father.

---

[139] Psalm 139:1-5; Proverbs 5:21.
[140] Psalm 93:1, 95:3; Jeremiah 23:20.
[141] Psalm 117:2; 1 Samuel 15:29.
[142] Exodus 34:6; Psalm 31:19; 1 Peter 1:3; John 3:16, 17:3.

"After the visitation from some angelic beings, you will leave the same way you came in and go to Bethany beyond the Jordan, where you were baptized. Your cousin John is still preaching and baptizing there. Some of the men I spoke about yesterday will be there, and they will accompany you to Galilee.[143]

"With them by your side, you will perform many signs and miracles throughout the next three-plus years that some will not agree with. I will summarize them now, and the Holy Spirit will unfold the rest as you go. Sometimes, you will need to take time alone to be refreshed in the spirit and rest. Please do so!"

Jesus nodded as he said, "I will, Father."

"Furthermore, when John has said all that needs to be said, you will call Simon Peter, Andrew, and John to follow you as you make the twenty-seven-hour journey north to Bethsaida along the western side of the Jordan River flat land.[144] This is when you will see Philip. Then on the third day, you will be invited to a wedding in Cana of Galilee, where all of you will join your mother, sisters, and brothers. When your mother tells you they have no wine, please listen to her, even though this is not the start of your ministry. However, this will be the first of many miracles."[145]

Jesus nodded slowly without speaking.

The sun had only peeked above the horizon when God continued to fill Jesus in with Philip, introducing Nathanael to Jesus after the wedding and before they would proceed to Jerusalem for Passover. This was the start of his Judea ministry. God told Jesus about what would happen when he entered the temple. He would find money changers taking advantage of those traveling from great distances. God said, "I permit you to do what you will, Jesus!"

---

[143] #7 on 60 Footsteps of Jesus handout.
[144] #8 on 60 Footsteps of Jesus handout.
[145] #9 on 60 Footsteps of Jesus handout.

Jesus became concerned about his Father's words, and a tear rolled down his face. After Jesus wiped it off with his finger, he said submissively, "I will have mercy on them."

God proceeded to speak, "You will have mercy, but only through anger will they learn!"

God continued, "In the temple court, you will predict your death and resurrection. This will be the first of three required times. While you are in Jerusalem at the Passover festival, many people will see the signs you perform and believe in the name of Jesus.

"You will meet a Pharisee named Nicodemus who is eager to know the truth and has been looking for the Messiah to come and free Israel from the bondage of Rome. He will be stubborn at first, but he comes to believe. Show him the way to the gate of the Kingdom of God.[146]

"When Passover is finished, you will head out to the countryside to start the first part of your Judean ministry, where you will preach the good news of salvation to many who will come to listen. Many will be baptized, so you must use the disciples to help you. You will cross paths with John the Baptist since he is still preaching his message of repentance in the region of Judea. He will point you out as the Son of God who takes away the world's sins. Many will accept you and want to hear your teachings.

"Peter, Andrew, James, John, Philip, and Nathanael will start to baptize those who turn toward your ministry instead of John's as you continue to proclaim the good news of salvation.[147]

"After some time has passed, you and your disciples will continue northward from Judea. Instead of taking the longer roundabout route through Perea, please take the shorter two-and-a-half-day journey, which is a direct route through the territory of Samaria near Sychar. As you approach

[146] #10 on 60 Footsteps of Jesus handout.
[147] #11 on 60 Footsteps of Jesus handout.

Jacob's well, send the disciples to Sychar to retrieve some food.

"When you reach the well, a woman will emerge from the village to draw water. Ask her for a drink. This will start a conversation leading her to believe you are Christ, the world's Savior. The fact is, she had five husbands, and the man she is with now is not her husband. She will return to her village, and many will turn to you and believe that the Messiah has come for the whole world, not just the Jews. Spend two days with them before heading north."[148]

Jesus once again nodded without a sound. By this time, the sun was high and scorching hot when Jesus rose and stretched his full height. In the distance, an antelope strolled by and the sight seemed to help Jesus refocus his thoughts as God continued to speak about the first preaching tour of his Galilean ministry.

As darkness came, a breeze sprung up, and scudding clouds blew across the sky, obscuring the moon occasionally. God left Jesus so he can honor the Sabbath. The next day when the Sabbath was over, Jesus spent the night praying and then got a good night's sleep.

That was the end of day twenty-four.

---

[148] #12 on 60 Footsteps of Jesus handout.

Chapter 8

The Itinerary Continued

A new day dawned on the world's Savior, and a profound loneliness, an oppressive emptiness, started to weigh heavily on his mind. All that had been said over the last weeks had played back in his mind through the night, and his face was drawn. For a moment, he wondered if this journey might not be worth it. Then, as he looked across the horizon into the morning sun, an unquestionably supernatural lift from his spirit overshadowed him. He remembered all that he and the Father had spoken about their creation from the beginning of time.

Jesus scurried up from the sandy surface he had used for a bed, brushed his clothing, threw his leather sandals on, and started his day off with a walk. He looked around and saw some of the beasts that called this part of the desert their home. Though they were beasts of prey to the commoner, they were friendly to the one who created them, and some of them approached him as if to say hello.

He knew at this point that the day would be great even though hunger pain already asserted itself strongly. At any moment, he would be graced with the presence of his Heavenly Father.

With his head held high, mouth curled, and a dance in his step, Jesus made a rotating movement to scan the area. It was the best he'd felt in three weeks. *That wasn't so bad,* he thought.

But then a voice came from the ground below his feet, "That's right, Jesus, puff up your chest. All of this is by your power. You don't need to be here; you can do this all on your own."

Jesus looked down and saw a slithering serpent wrapping around his feet. Within a blink of an eye, Jesus recalled a Psalm of David: *Sit at my right hand until I make your enemies a footstool for your feet.*[149] Jesus lifted his foot as he continued, and as he placed it on the head of the serpent, it slithered under the sand and disappeared.

Returning to a square stance, Jesus shook his head in amazement and gave out a laugh. Returning to his walk, he patiently waited to hear his Father's voice. Jesus thought about the night before last when, before finding a place to rest, he had asked God to tell him more about James.

"Father, before you leave, you mentioned James the other day. Tell me more!"

"I would love to, Jesus."

"James, at first, will misunderstand your ministry and not be a believer.[150] He will be in and out of the ministry as you travel, and he will question some of the things he hears and sees. After your resurrection and before the ascension, you will visit him.[151] He will believe everything when he sees you in your divine nature. He will then go to Jerusalem and be one of the first witnesses of your resurrection. After your ascension, he will stay there and form part of the group of believers who will pray in the upper room.[152] From that time forward, James' status within the Jerusalem church grows, and he will become an apostle, nicknamed, the Just.[153]

"Just after Saul is converted, Saul will meet with him and Peter about some of the details needed to build the

---

[149] Psalm 110.

[150] John 7:5.

[151] 1 Corinthians 15:7.

[152] Acts 1:14.

[153] James was called "the Just" because of his ascetic practices, which involved taking Nazarite vows.

church.[154] Several years later, when Peter escapes from prison, he will report to James about the miraculous manner of the escape.[155] James will be the apparent chairman to the Jerusalem council in Peter's defense.[156] He will become an elder, a pillar of the church.[157]

"James will author a letter written to a Jewish Christian audience that will deal more with Christian ethics than Christian theology. Its theme will be the outworking of faith—the external evidence of internal conversion.

"And as I mentioned to you before, James will be thrown off a temple when he refuses to deny his faith in you, survive, and then be beaten to death with a club."[158]

Jesus then wept for his brother a second time before resting.

• • •

In the present day, the sky darkened with clouds to relieve Jesus of the sun's rays, and he heard his Father's voice beside him, "Jesus, I am proud of you, my son! Even though this time on earth as the Son of Man is playing with your mind, you are strong and courageous. Now that you have overcome the flesh, the Holy Spirit will remain in you. I know you will endure all that comes your way and make it to the end."

Jesus let out a sigh of relaxation.

With Jesus ready to receive more direction that will be needed, God said, "Jesus, I would like to continue where I left off before I told you about James. Again, this next part will take us through another week of your itinerary. As you

---

[154] Galatians 1:19.

[155] Acts 12:17.

[156] Acts 15:13.

[157] Galatians 2:9.

[158] Although there is no Biblical record, according to the first-century historian, Josephus, second-century historian, Heqesippus, Apocalypse of James, & Ecclesiastical History, 1995, pp. 75-76.

recall, I mentioned recorded miracle number eleven, the healing of the centurion's servant. Afterward, you will start the second preaching tour of Galilee with many more healings and followers.

"After some time, you will travel back to Nazareth for another try. The last time you were there they rejected you because their hearts were hardened. Though some will reject you again, I want to give others one more opportunity, if not then, later, to accept the man they grew up with and was known as a compassionate, caring, and hard worker.[159]

"After shaking the dust off, you will start the third preaching tour of the Galilean ministry by teaching the Word to surrounding villages before sending the disciples out alone. At this point of your ministry, they have been with you for almost two years, and you will need to see how much they learned by sending them out two-by-two."[160]

Jesus asked, "Will I be disappointed?"

God replied, "Even though they have been with you for almost two years, they will still need to learn more."

Meanwhile, the afternoon sun tried to break through the covering God had placed over Jesus. Not even the still air was a match for the two creators of the world as Jesus paused for a breath.

It will be around this time of Jesus's ministry when John the Baptist would be beheaded by the order of King Herod Antipater because his wife, Herodias, nursed a grudge against John and wanted to kill him. Knowing how much Jesus loved his cousin, God spent some time telling him about those tragic events. The king would marry his brother Philip's wife, Herodias, and John would rebuke Herod for it because it would not be lawful for him to have her. God said, "Both will want to kill John but will not be able to because the king will fear John and will protect him because he is a righteous and holy man. That is when Herodias will

[159] #29 on 60 Footsteps of Jesus handout.
[160] #30 on 60 Footsteps of Jesus handout.

scheme with her daughter, whereby she will force her husband's hand. On Herod's birthday, the daughter will dance for the king and all his guests. Since the king will be drunk and it will please him, he will make an oath to give her whatever she asks. Prompted by her mother, she will say, 'Give me here on a platter the head of John the Baptist.'"[161]

When Jesus heard these words, his heart thudded in his chest as he fell to his knees and wept. After some time, knowing that this would be part of the plan and there would be nothing he could say or do, Jesus rose to his feet and dried the tears off his face. That is when God told him that when his disciples returned from their mission, they would be exhausted and weary, and he would need to take them to a quiet location near Bethsaida for time alone to comfort them and himself.

Afterward, he would be interrupted by a large crowd of people where, after teaching them all day, thousands will be fed after blessing five loaves and two fishes. This is the enduring lesson of feeding the five thousand for recorded miracle number nineteen, and it will become the most astounding miracle of all.[162]

As God spent hours with his Son, telling him all that would be needed, he got to the point when Jesus would cross back to the Magadan/Dalmanutha region. Some Pharisees and Sadducees would join him by asking for a sign from heaven. The Savior sighed deeply! "Why are they so blind when the greatest sign of all will be standing before them?"[163]

God agreed with Jesus, and continued, "Furthermore, when you reach Bethsaida, you will heal a blind man, which will be recorded as miracle number twenty-five.[164] Then travel north to Caesarea Philippi in Iturea and Trachonitis

---

[161] Matthew 14:1-12.
[162] #31 on 60 Footsteps of Jesus handout.
[163] #37 on 60 Footsteps of Jesus handout.
[164] #38 on 60 Footsteps of Jesus handout.

for some alone time with the disciples. This will allow you to ask them serious questions about whom they think you are, and along the way, Peter will confess that you are Christ.[165]

"After a six-day journey, turn toward Mount Hermon. Take Peter, James, and John with you to the top of the mountain for a special meeting. They will be good disciples and friends to you, my son, even with their unbelief sometimes, so I want them to see you in your deity. Not only will they hear my voice, but they will also meet Elijah and Moses, representing the Old Testament saints. Peter, James, and John will represent the New Testament saints. And you, my Son, will be in the middle. I cannot wait to have you all together in one place!"[166]

Jesus turned and uttered, "I love when you are happy, Father!" At that very moment, all the animals that had gathered around Jesus laid down to pay tribute to the Creator.

When God closed in on the third year of Jesus' ministry, he told him to remain in the Galilee area for some time because the Jewish leaders in Judea would seek to kill him, and he would send word when it was safe to return to Judea for the final days of his time on Earth.

As sundown approached on day thirty-one, Jesus made his way to a cleft in a rock as the warmth faded away like mist dissolving in sunlight.

Jesus was past the crucial part of his fast. His body was not fighting him like in previous days, and there was still much to talk about, so they decided to make it an all-nighter.

His Heavenly Father spoke to him all night with the different teachings needed throughout his ministry. Some of those teachings would be the parables, about prayer, asking for a sign, warning about religious hypocrisy, and against the teaching of the Pharisees. They discussed topics that will

[165] #39 on 60 Footsteps of Jesus handout.
[166] #40 on 60 Footsteps of Jesus handout.

need to be taught in the temple and to the disciples about the last days and much more.

The next day when sunset came, God left Jesus to honor the Sabbath and told him he would see him in the morrow of the following day.

That was the end of day thirty-two.

Chapter 9
The Itinerary Finale

It was the morning of the last week Jesus would be spending in the wilderness, and the sun had broken through the drab sky, and the cool air warmed quickly. Knowing there were only days left in the desert, he was able to fight off his body's hunger.

As Jesus moved about the desert, God returned to finish up with his instructions.

"Jesus, now that we have gone over all the teachings that will be needed, I would like to finish with the itinerary. This last part will be the same as the last couple of weeks. If you need to rest, please do so."

Jesus nodded. "I am doing great, Father. My body is no longer fighting me, and I have plenty of energy."

With that, God continued to speak, "Jesus, as the Feast of Tabernacles approaches, I will give you the word to leave Galilee for the last time in human form. You will make your way back down to Jerusalem by traveling through Samaria. They will be inhospitable to you, even with all that was done at the well. Continue your journey! Some of the disciples will react angrily, rebuke them and travel to another village.

"When you reach Jerusalem, it will be the Feast of Tabernacles. You cannot attend publicly but will do so secretly because it will not be your time. A few days before the festival ends, go to the outside area of the temple to teach. Some of what we spoke about the other night will be taught there. Many will marvel at your knowledge of the Old Testament, and your teaching ability will attract their attention.

93

"Just before the feast is over, walk to the Mount of Olives for the night. Then on the morrow, walk down the side of Olivet, cross over the Kidron Valley, and climb back into the city, where the temple is located. There, many will gather to hear you teach. The scribes and the Pharisees will try to trick you into saying something wrong. They will bring you a woman who was caught in the act of adultery and will make her stand in the middle of the crowd. They want to see if you will contradict the Law of Moses."[167]

This point of Jesus' ministry will be the start of the latter part of Jesus' Judean ministry. After Jesus stayed in Jerusalem until the Feast of Dedication, there will only be a few weeks left before he returned to heaven and is seated on the right hand of the Father.

"Furthermore," continued God, "you will leave Jerusalem and go to Bethany beyond the Jordan, Bethabara, where you were baptized, and stay there for a while. There you will teach the people about entering the Kingdom of God, the willingness to put Jehovah above anyone and anything, about compassion for the lost, focusing on Elohim and Law, and about the importance of forgiveness and a faith-filled attitude of service to God. Then you will get word that your friend Lazarus has fallen ill and died."[168]

Jesus's mind started to wander from what his Father was saying with memories of his friendship with Lazarus. God knew that Jesus was sidetracked with his emotions, so he hesitated momentarily. Meanwhile, the morning air was quickly replaced with thick air with no breeze. Thankfully, God still had a silky-smooth cloak thrown over the area Jesus had been walking.

After Jesus regained his thoughts, God comforted his son and then continued, "Do not rush to get to Bethany because we will use this for my glory. After a few days, when you arrive, you will perform a spectacular miracle by raising

[167] #42 on 60 Footsteps of Jesus handout.
[168] #45 and 46 on 60 Footsteps of Jesus handout.

your dear friend from the grave. It will cause a great commotion in Jerusalem and the surrounding villages that will help the Pharisees who do not believe in you plan the final steps to your arrest. This will be remembered and talked about for generations."

Because of the commotion in Jerusalem, God told Jesus that he will need to flee to a village called Ephraim with his disciples. Then travel northward along the border of Galilee and Samaria, where he will heal ten men with leprosy. Then he will meet up with some pilgrims traveling to Jerusalem for Passover through Perea on the east side of the Jordan River flat land. After they reached Perea, he will teach the crowds about divorce, the importance of the Kingdom of God for little children, that one is saved by Elohim's seemingly impossible grace in Jesus and not by works, and that grace is given to all equally.[169]

A short time later, they will head toward Jerusalem by way of Jericho for the final week before Jesus's death. For the Sabbath, they will stop at the house of Martha, Mary, and Lazarus in Bethany to have dinner and be anointed by Mary. Because it will be the Sabbath, and the written law includes that not even the animals are to work on the Sabbath, Jesus will not enter Jerusalem until the 10th of Nisan.[170]

God said after all that, "You will send two disciples into the village opposite you on the 10th of Nisan for a donkey to use as your triumphal entry. I will already have arranged the use of the colt from the owner by sending an angel to him beforehand. You and the disciples will stay in Bethany on the Mount of Olives during the watch[171] for the rest of the week and travel to the temple daily."

Jesus nodded without speaking.

---

[169] #47, 48, and 49 on 60 Footsteps of Jesus handout.
[170] #50, 51, and 52 on 60 Footsteps of Jesus handout.
[171] 1st watch: 6pm-9pm, 2nd watch: 9pm-12am, 3rd watch: 12am-3am, 4th watch: 3am-6am.

"Now, here is your itinerary for the week: After the disciples return with the colt, they will remove their cloaks and place them on the colt as a makeshift saddle. When the time is right, Jesus, you will mount the virgin colt and start for Jerusalem. You will enter the city in kechom ha-yom[172] by the east gate.

"Many people will gather and walk with you in excitement and spontaneously pay homage by spreading their outer cloaks before you on the dusty road, in the same manner that had been done when Jehu declared to the princes of Israel that he was anointed king of Israel, they hastened, and took every man his garment, and put it under him. Others will spread green branches, also known as palm branches, that were cut from surrounding fields along the path.

"Along the way, and as everyone enters the city, they will shout, 'Hosanna to the Son of David! Blessed is he who comes in the name of the Lord! Hosanna in the highest!' But the leaders of the temple will despise you."[173]

For the remainder of the conversation, God gave every detail of that last week. When they got to the part where Jesus would have dinner at Simon the leper's house, where a woman would anoint him for a second anointing, God also spoke about Judas Iscariot, reminding Jesus of their conversation a couple of weeks earlier. This will be where Judas would leave to make plans with the chief priests, the scribes, and the elders of the people assembled at the high priest's palace, called Caiaphas, who will pay him thirty pieces of silver to seal the deal to betray him. With deep compassion, Jesus lowered his chin to the ground and wept again for the loss of a soul.

As they went through *Maundy Thursday*, the day of unleavened bread, God gave every detail of the Last Supper.

---

[172] In the heat of the day (Genesis 18:1) refers to the early afternoon when the sun is at its strongest.

[173] #53 on 60 Footsteps of Jesus handout covers the whole week.

Afterward, God gave Jesus the account of his last act as a free man.

"Then you will comfort the disciples before leaving for Gethsemane, a garden at the foot of the Mount of Olives, with the teachings that we spoke about the other night. After you are finished, you will leave for Gethsemane, where you will be arrested. When you get there, you will take Peter, James, and John with you to keep watch while you spend time with me.

"Then, as you are praying, Judas Iscariot will come with a great multitude to arrest you. When Judas sees you, he will approach you with a kiss. This will let them know you are the one they have been looking for. Peter will stand up to defend you, and when he does, he will cut the right ear off of Malchus, one of the servants of the high priest. Please put it back on since he only follows orders and does not deserve that kind of treatment."

Jesus replied, "Oh, Peter will be a handful."

God answered, "Yes, he will, but we love him no matter what. Everyone who has been with you will disperse with the fear of being arrested too. Then you will be taken to Annas, the father-in-law of Caiaphas, who will ask you some questions. Then Annas will send you bound to Caiaphas, the high priest, who will question you deeper. At this time, Peter will disown you three times as the rooster crows after he is recognized as one of your followers."

God finished speaking about the trial Jesus would undergo at the Praetorium. They talked about Pontius Pilate, who would send him to King Herod who will be visiting Jerusalem at that time. Herod would see no fault in Jesus but would mock him and send him back to Pilate with a purple robe like a king would wear. When the people insist Jesus be crucified, Pilate will pronounce his sentence that their demand should be carried out.

With that, God walked Jesus through the last footsteps he would take as a man. This was not an easy conversation to have since it talked about an act that God hoped from the beginning of creation would not be necessary. "Jesus, they will have a cross already built for you to carry to Golgotha, where executions occur. This will be a brutal journey, even though it is only five thousand cubits.[174] It will take you over an hour to reach the hill. You will be beaten, spit on, and mocked. After they make fun of you, they will take the robe off and dress you in your clothes.

"The road will be hilly and exhausting from the beatings and lashing, and you will feel worn out by spiritual suffering. You will find it hard to walk and will fall to your knees from the weight of the cross a few times. A great multitude of people will follow. Among the people will be many women who will weep and lament for you. When you get to the hill, I will put in the soldiers' hearts to allow a man named Simon, a Cyrenian, who will be compassionately watching you, to carry the cross for you. He is a strong man who believes in you and will help you bear the cross until you reach the top.

"When you get to the area, they will place you between two robbers that have already been crucified. When raised, they will continue to mock you, wag their heads, and say, 'You who destroy the temple and build it in three days, save Yourself! If You are the Son of God, come down from the cross.' Even one of the robbers will agree with them. But the other one will receive you as Christ and enter the kingdom when he dies.

"Just before you take your last breath as a man, your face will look worn out and tired as the weight of all the people's sins will be placed on your slender shoulders. It will be like no other feeling you've ever felt. No matter how you feel, I will be right there with you, Jesus! You will know that all things have been accomplished through the Scripture by saying, '*I thirst!*'"

Just as God spoke those words, Jesus's mouth fell open as he looked down at the ground, and he didn't blink for at least twenty heartbeats. His face looked worn out and tired

---

[174] Two and one-half miles.

as if he felt the weight of the whole world on his slender shoulders for real. As tears of sorrow and joy mixed, Jesus whispered, "Father, may your will be done!"

As God looked at his son with tears rolling down his cheeks, he reached out with loving arms and pulled him close. "When all has been fulfilled, I will send Joseph of Arimathea, the disciple who followed you secretly, for fear of the Jews. He will ask Pilate that he might take away your body, and Pilate will permit him. Nicodemus, who came to you at night during Passover, will bring a mixture of myrrh and aloes. Then they will take your body and bind it in strips of linen with the spices, as the custom of the Jews is to bury. They will put you in a new tomb owned by Joseph of Arimathea. This is when you will go to Hades to retrieve our Kingdom's keys from Lucifer just before I raise you back to life. "Jesus, this will complete your last week as a man."

Jesus shifted his feet, rubbed his eyes, stretched his full height with his arms outstretched, and yelled, "Alleluia!" as God retreated to heaven. Even the animals were running around dancing, praising Jesus.

It was almost too dark to see by that time, so Jesus remained where he was. He lowered himself to the ground and rested his head against the side of a rock for the night.

Shortly after he closed his eyes, Jesus felt a tap on his shoulders. "Wake up, Jesus." Jesus opened one eye and saw an old man standing in front of him. As he opened the other eye he heard, "All this time you walked around like you are fine with this. No one in their right mind does that! Get angry, Jesus, curse your Father for making you go through this; just once, Jesus, it will make you feel like a man!"

Paying the voice no mind, Jesus closed his eyes, quoted from the Ten Commandments, and said, "Honour thy father..."[175] He trailed off as he fell back to sleep.

[175] Exodus 20:12 KJV.

After almost four weeks of God handing down the layout of Jesus' ministry, Jesus rested for the night, through the next day, and through the Sabbath.

That was the end of day thirty-nine.

The following section is about the temptations Jesus experienced on the last day of his forty-day fast according to the Gospels. The account of each temptation is scriptural, and some of the actual Scripture conversations are genuine, but the added imaginary dialog will make the story fiction.

We will start off with temptation number one. Satan knew Jesus was hungry and commanded him to turn some stones into bread by questioning his deity.

For the second temptation, Satan took Jesus to the highest point of the temple and commanded him to jump, telling him that the angels would save him and not even his foot would touch a stone.

For the last and final temptation, Satan brought Jesus to the top of a large mountain overlooking the kingdom that Satan controlled and commanded Jesus to bow down before him and worship him. In exchange, Satan would give him the kingdoms of the world.

Each account has been extended beyond the few words found in the Gospels. This is not to disregard the writers of the Gospels but to bring a storytelling meaning behind the dialog between Jesus and Satan.

• • •

A Small Commentary!

But why was Jesus tempted?

Part of the answer is to be an example for us. It may seem strange that Jesus should be led into the wilderness to be tempted. But this temptation was necessary to demonstrate his moral fitness to do the work for which he had come into the world.

There are three temptations that are accounted for in the Gospel of Matthew. With the first test, Jesus was tempted to depend on his own independent provision of food rather than to rely on God. The second temptation involved performing a miracle to show Christ's supernatural power and draw attention to himself. It was the temptation to abuse his power for his own benefit. In the third test, Jesus was tempted to secure an earthly crown and bypass the suffering and sacrifice he would endure on the cross.

Many Bible scholars suggest that the specific temptations Jesus faced in the wilderness represent three main categories of all human temptation: *"The lust of the flesh, the lust of the eyes, and the pride of life"* (1 John 2:16).

Jesus intentionally agreed with his Father to be tempted in all the ways that humanity is tempted to sin in this fallen world. Rather than being a distant God who doesn't relate much to humanity, Jesus is "God with us."

Temptation itself is not a sin. Jesus was "tempted in every way, just as we are—yet he did not sin" (Hebrews. 4:15; 2 Corinthians 5:21). The Lord was not tested to see if he would fail. Jesus was led into the wilderness by the Spirit to demonstrate how we can resist the temptation to sin, and how, through Christ's power, we, too, can overcome.

It was because he was human and made like us in every way that he could do three vital things:

1) Destroy Satan's power and free those held in slavery by their fear of death (Hebrews 2:15).
2) Become a merciful and faithful High Priest in service to God and atone for our sins (Hebrews 2:17).
3) Be the one who can sympathize with us in all our weaknesses and infirmities (Hebrews 4:15).

Our Lord's human nature enables him to sympathize with our weaknesses because he was also subjected to weakness. More importantly, we have a High Priest who is able to intercede on our behalf and provide the grace of forgiveness.

It is important to remember that Jesus is God, and that God cannot sin. Indeed, he was also human; however, to say that he could sin as a human but not as God is to build a case without a scriptural foundation. Jesus could be tempted from without. Satan came to him with suggestions contrary to the will of God. But unlike us, he could not be tempted from within—no sinful lusts or passions could originate in him. Furthermore, nothing in him would respond to Satan's seductions (John 14:30).

Despite Jesus' inability to sin, the temptation was genuine. It was possible for him to be faced with enticements to sin, but it was morally impossible for him to yield. He could only do what he saw the Father doing (John 5:19), and it is inconceivable that he would ever see the Father sinning. He could do nothing on his own authority (John 5:30), and the Father would never give him the authority to yield to temptation.

The purpose of the temptation was not to see if he would sin but to prove that even under tremendous pressure, he could do nothing but obey the Word of God.

If Jesus could sin as a human being, we would face the problem of his still being human in heaven. Could he still sin? Obviously, no!

What does that mean for us?

Jesus overcame every temptation by choosing to trust in God's Word. Each time Satan tempted Jesus to sin, Jesus confronted Satan with biblical truth by declaring, "*It is written*," and then quoting Scripture. Jesus fought each spiritual battle with the power of God's Word, and good triumphed over evil. We can learn from Jesus' example to rely on the Bible's words of wisdom when facing temptation.

The temptation of Jesus shows us that, no matter how intensely we are tempted to sin, we can overcome that temptation. Rather than relying on our own limited willpower, we can do so by relying on God, who will faithfully help us.

Christ's experience in the wilderness serves as an example for Christian disciples. But as we study the account, an even deeper meaning is revealed. We see that God allows his followers to be tested for a good purpose. The Spirit led Jesus into the wilderness to be tempted because God wanted his son and his followers to understand the Lord's messianic mission clearly—that Christ had not come to earth as Israel's Conquering King but as her Suffering Servant.

Hope you enjoy the extended imaginary in the temptation stories brought to you through the imaginary mind of
the author.

Scene 3—Day/Night 40

Chapter 10

Lust of the Flesh

The end of Jesus's journey in the wilderness drew near. Outside of the temptations, forty days had passed since he had seen anyone face-to-face outside of his Heavenly Father and the appearance of his earthly father, Joseph. Under a pale moon, Jesus started to make his way to the area he had originally entered the wilderness. His lean face in the moonlight was a ghastly sight. As he reflected on the days gone by, he could not help but weep. He knew that all the Father had shown him needed to be fulfilled, but he wondered if his love for the people would be enough to overcome the world.

"Will the people listen to me and understand my teachings? Or will they still follow the old covenant and their old way of thinking? Will they believe the miracles when they see them? How hard is it really going to be with the disciples? Will they believe that I am truly the Son of God? The great I AM! I hope this flesh can bear the crucifixion and not be as bad as my Father said it would be."

These are some of the questions Jesus asked himself as he walked the dusty road north.

His path was rocky, causing an occasional stumble. As daylight approached, he felt hungry and could not wait until he reached a place with something to eat. He remembered seeing a fig tree on his way into the wilderness and hoped some figs were still hanging.

As the sun rose, Jesus sat on a large rock to rest; his thoughts were interrupted by a figure in the distance. He wiped his eyes to get the dust out, and when he took his hands away, a beautiful figure was standing in front of him. Taking a deep breath, he rose to his feet with a wide-eyed look and trying not to make eye contact.

Then a voice, sharp and clear, said, "Jesus, do you know why I am here?"

"Yes, my Father had warned me you were coming. He said you would come to test me," Jesus answered.

"The Spirit has led you here and has allowed you to know how it feels to be tested by me. But to do this, you have to give up every privilege that has been given to you. You must be like a human in every way, selfish, alone, and little.

"Man thinks they are intelligent with high levels of motivation and self-awareness but are also highly fallible. They are filled with emotions that dictate their lives. They lie, cheat, and backstab every chance they get. They develop and build tools, clothing, and buildings, making them helpless without these technologies. They say they want to live in peace but always find themself in war and conflict. They call themself a family but do not know how to love. They play and make everything a joke. They put more emphasis on their culture and heritage, but they are just despicable little creatures who are fiercely competitive, living in sin."

With his face drawn and tired looking, Jesus looked down to the sand as he listened.

"Walk away from the protection that lies within you, Jesus. None of that can help you here! Be separated from the divinity so you can experience true testing." Then with a sour expression, he added, "You know it is necessary, Jesus, it is the only way we can challenge each other."

Jesus muttered, "Father, thank you for your protection."

Then the beautiful image disappeared, and shortly afterward, Satan returned in its place with his left hand in his pocket and wearing a smirk. "Jesus, you do not look so good. Are you hungry?"

"Yes," Jesus murmured.

As Satan moved closer to Jesus with a sour face, knowing that Jesus was hungry and at his weakest point of exhaustion, physically, mentally, and maybe even spiritually, he stooped down to pick up stones from the sand and said, "If you are the Son of God, command that these stones become bread."[176]

Satan knew who Jesus was but phrased his words to a question instead of saying, "Since you are the Son of God..." The devil was alluding to the words of the Father to Jesus at his baptism when the voice from heaven said, "This is my beloved Son."[177] Satan challenged Jesus to prove that he was the Son of God through miraculous works. He wanted Jesus to use his divine powers to make something to eat.

Jesus looked at the stones in Satan's hands and then looked up into the eyes of Satan and said, "You call upon my Father's power?"

"You have the power to command these stones, don't you, Jesus?" Satan replied.

Jesus looked at the stones again, then looked right into the face of Satan and said, "If I do as you say, I will not be doing my Father's will because I only do what I see the Father do. I will not abuse his power."

"I am just asking for bread to relieve your hunger, Jesus," Satan said in a sarcastic tone.

Jesus answered with an authoritative look and quoted from Deuteronomy 8:3, "It is written and forever remains written, 'Man shall not live by bread alone; but man lives by every word that proceeds from the mouth of the Lord.'"

As soon as Jesus finished speaking, Satan disappeared.

• • •

A Short Commentary!

To fulfill a natural appetite by using divine power in response to Satan's prompting is in direct disobedience to God. The idea behind the suggestion is an echo of (Genesis

[176] Matthew 4:3.
[177] Matthew 3:17.

3:6). One of the books written by the Apostle John classifies this temptation as the lust of the flesh (1 John 2:16). Since Jesus had received no instructions from the Father to turn stones into bread, he would not act on his own and thus obey Satan, no matter how intense his hunger.

Chapter 11

The Pride of Life

With his face showing fatigue and his eyes blood-shot with the morning sun's glare, Jesus kept walking along the western side of the Jordan River toward the northern part of the Judean Wilderness.

He recalled Lucifer's residence in heaven. "Why did he have to do what he did? Lucifer was created as an anointed cherub with four wings and four faces and large in size with tremendous power. He was filled with intelligence, wisdom, and a mild personality. He was perfect in beauty from the day he was created. We considered him a bright morning star and the greatest of all my Father's creations before mankind until his pride got the best of him. The desire for honor and glory that belonged to God alone was unnecessary."

By that time, the sun was high and scorching hot. It seemed time stood still for a moment as Jesus was engrossed in his thoughts as he stopped to rest. Almost overcome by sheer exhaustion, beads of perspiration stood on his still face.

Jesus continued aloud with his thoughts, "How could the highest and most exalted angel believe he could be greater than his Creator?" Jesus looked on in amazement as he yelled out, "Jealousy! The creature that was liked and more powerful than all the other angels became jealous."

After the first attempt failed, Satan returned for his second attempt and interrupted Jesus' thoughts, striking at the heart of Jesus' previous victory. He stood before Jesus with an obstinate scowl. He waved his arm as if it was a magic wand to reveal Jerusalem and them standing at the pinnacle of the temple,[178] the southern corner of the temple where the priests would blow the shofar to announce the coming of the Sabbath. Below about ninety-three cubits would be a bustling intersection with many vendor shops and a large milling crowd.

Satan turned from Jesus as they looked out over the temple courts, raised his arms, and yelled, "There is one way to get them to notice you as their Messiah, Jesus. You must convince them that you are sent by God by achieving glory without suffering. If you are the Son of God, throw yourself down!" He pointed to the ground. "For it is written: 'He will command his angels to serve, care for, protect and watch over you. They will catch you, Jesus, and lift you up in their wings so that you will not strike your foot against a stone.'[179] Then the people will see through this spectacular sign of your divine Sonship that there is someone they can listen to."

As Jesus looked out, Satan added, "They will listen to someone who can do that! Right, Jesus?" Satan nodded emphatically.

Jesus muttered, "Do not test God for your own purposes."

Then Jesus responded by also quoting Scripture and applying it correctly. "It is not my Father's will. He would not have sent me if he had someone to test his laws. On the other hand, it is written and forever remains written, 'You shall not tempt the Lord your God.'"[180]

As soon as Jesus finished speaking, Satan disappeared for a second time.

• • •

A Short Commentary!

---

[178] Matthew 4:5.
[179] Matthew 4:6.
[180] Matthew 4:7.

Being cast to the busy street below and then carried up by the angels would have been a fitting location to announce his Messiahship. It would have been an easy way to receive glory, (Deuteronomy 6:16). John described this appeal as "the pride of life" (1 John 2:16). This temptation comes to us in the desire to attain religious prominence apart from the fellowship of his suffering. We seek great things for ourselves and then run and hide when difficulties come our way. When we ignore God's will and exalt ourselves, we tempt God.

Chapter 12

The Lust of the Eyes

After Satan left, Jesus continued his thoughts before the interruption. "Jealousy! When I sat at the right hand of my Father in the throne room of heaven, and all the angelic beings would come in singing, 'Holy, holy, holy is the Lord of hosts.' Lucifer's pride started to turn on him. He started to disapprove because he liked being the center of attention with the other angels and did not like when they bowed before the throne. I started to see the anger on his face more and more.

"What really set him off was not being part of the creative committee and not being invited to the creation planning meeting. He heard of the meeting and asked if he could join since he was a top angel. The truth was that he thought he was just as important as his Creator and wanted to know every plan and thought of God.

"Filled with anger and discontent, he quickly went out of the throne room. The likes we have never seen before. After he gathered all the other angels, he voiced his anger by telling them he was no longer going to worship my Father and me. He was going to be the new god, and they should all worship him instead. Of course, not all the angels agreed with him because they knew their place and were dedicated to us. They even tried to put some sense into Lucifer and all who wanted to follow him.

"He would not pay them any mind and proceeded to make his own plans for a better-than-ever government where they would all have total opportunity and freedom to do as they please. The loyal angels again tried to warn

Lucifer about the consequences of his actions, but he was more confident than ever that he was doing the right thing for himself, for the angels that chose to follow him, and for the heavens.

"When my Father heard of this treacherous act, he called everyone together to address the issue. Father allowed Lucifer to speak his reasoning for treason, reminding him that his misconduct was inexcusable. The first thing out of Lucifer's mouth was how we no longer cared about him. He felt abandoned since he was not invited to the meeting, and the lack of importance made him feel unwanted. Father allowed him to speak for a good amount of time, and no matter how much we tried to show him the error in his ways, he brushed it off and sat with his wings folded and with an obstinate scowl.

"At that moment, Father pointed out that if Lucifer kept up with his rebellion, he would have no choice but to punish him. Lucifer asked what his punishment would be, and when he heard that he would be unworthy of heaven, Lucifer then yelled out that a third of his angels were on his side and challenged Father, claiming God would not be willing to cast out that many of his angels.

"That is when it happened! Father stood up and demanded that Lucifer and all who followed him be banished from heaven forever. The heavens shook as they all made their way out from the presence of God and to the earth. Afterward, all was peaceful in heaven once again."

Jesus continued with his thoughts, "And what was worse, when he left, millions of others pledged their allegiance to Lucifer and followed him because they thought he had something of value. They are going to be upset when they learn their true position."

Jesus stopped, lifted his head to heaven, and called out to his Father, "Give me strength to continue this journey, Father."

With the mid-afternoon burning sky, Jesus covered his head to help ease the fire-like sensation. He knew he was on

THE ITINERARY · 117

the last day and was looking forward to the next day when he left this desolate place. As a man, he had felt more compassionate and caring to humanity and more submissive to his Father. He enjoyed his time with the animals but yearned for the companionship of others. His dreamy thoughts drifted off to when his Father had told him about all the ones who would be with him to minister to the region.

Once again, his thoughts were interrupted by Satan's return, and Satan said in a desperate voice, "Jesus, you do not understand the stakes; let me show you."

Then, with a wave of his arm again, Satan put a vision of them standing on an exceedingly high mountain and showed him all the world's kingdoms.[181]

With his arms wide open and a wrathful glare, he said, "Look, Jesus, this is all mine. I have glory over every kingdom and all the nations. Power! Jesus! Power! No longer am I in second in command. I'm number one. You never felt that power. I have!" Satan closed his eyes and tilted his head down. "You never were able to understand...until now. Now you can be NUMBER ONE!"

It was the first time, as a man, that Jesus witnessed Satan behave this way, and Satan's snarling face completely spellbound him.

"Do you know what that means, Jesus?" Satan added.

"No," Jesus replied, shaking his head with disgust. With a piercing glare, Jesus turned his head back and stared into the face of the enemy.

Satan added, "Power is what every man wants more than anything else in the world. They kill for it! There is nothing more precise, and it is yours to have."

"Bow down to me, Jesus. Just once!"[182] Satan's stern look radiated power. "In all of existence before and after time, just once, Jesus! It is a small price considering the reward."

[181] Matthew 4:8.
[182] Matthew 4:9.

Jesus knew in his heart that the spiritual birthright for the passing glory of this world and to worship and serve the creature rather than the Creator was not his Father's will.

Jesus looked annoyed and yelled with the utmost compassion, " Away with you, Satan! For it is written, 'You shall worship the Lord your God, and him only you shall serve.'"[183]

Then Satan left him for the last time.[184]

• • •

A Short Commentary!

With their grandeur, the reward offered for all the kingdoms of the world appealed to "The lust of the eyes" (1 John 2:16). In a sense, the kingdoms of the world does belong to Satan at present. He is spoken of as the god of this age (2 Corinthians 4:4), and John tells us that the "whole world lies under the sway of the wicked one" (1 John 5:19). When Jesus appears at the second coming, the kingdom of the world becomes his. Jesus would not violate the divine timetable; he would certainly never worship Satan!

---

[183] Matthew 4:10.
[184] Matthew 4:11.

Chapter 13

Ministering Angels

A s soon as the third temptation was lost, Satan left. Jesus won because he recognized Satan's attack mode of lies and deception. Jesus had fulfilled all that was needed to prepare him for his ministry, and God sent angels to take care of the last part of this journey.

The sunset was approaching, and ministering angels appeared. The desire that morning of going to the fig tree was no longer necessary.

His fasting and hunger were physical and tangible, yet during the forty days of fasting, these holy beings stayed away while the battle was being fought lest they should seem to steal some of the honors of the victory. When the duel ended, God commanded them to hasten to bring food for the body and comfort for the mind of the champion King.

First appeared the archangels, Michael and Gabriel. As they appeared before Jesus, they humbly bowed before the Lord with admiration and grace. At first, no word was spoken until Jesus touched them on their heads and commanded them to rise.

Then Michael, as the constant defender of the Jewish people, spoke first, "Lord, it is so good to see you." He handed Jesus a cup of water. "It is our privilege to come before you to help you prepare for your ministry. We have brought you drink and food for the body and will comfort you in any area needed. When you walk out of here, you will not look the same, and it will be as if you never hungered or thirsted."

Then Gabriel said joyfully, "As you know, Lord, we were created to serve, and today we serve the servant. The beings from my team will provide you with a king's banquet. Everything on the table will be exactly what your human body needs after a forty-day fast to build strength for the next journey. They even have food for the animals that followed you and kept you company."

Michael chimed in again, "Lord, as you feast and build strength, others will be preparing a proper place of rest. We know you have not had comfortable bedding outside the sand and rocks to lay your head, so they will build you proper bedding for when you turn in."

"Lord," Gabriel said, "even though you are in a desolate place with little rain for water, some angels will draw you a tub of water in a secluded place to freshen up. We also have a new set of garments, complete with a seamless tunic, leather sandals, shawl, and a staff."

As both archangels turn away from Jesus, they said, "You will be treated with royalty as you so deserve. Good night, my Lord!"

Jesus was endowed with tremendous physical strength and the inner power of the Spirit to enter his ministry and fulfill everything God had called him to do. The victory was his as the forty days ended and all temptations and lies conquered. With Jesus overcoming the tempter, Lucifer, it pushed his divine nature to the forefront along with all the spiritual power that such entails.

This was just the start of all Jesus did for all humanity, and the story does not end here!

• • •

A Short Commentary!

Temptation is never as great as when one has made a public declaration of faith, just as did our Lord when He was baptized in the Jordan (Matthew 3:13-17). However, we also note that, during this time of exhaustive testing, our Lord was also ministered to by angels, a mystery indeed that the omnipotent one should condescend to receive such help from lesser beings! During times of testing and trial, we, too, are aided by angels who are ministering spirits sent to those who will inherit salvation (Hebrews 1:14). Here is a beautiful description of the ministry that his people also benefit from.

The ministry of angels can be found throughout the life of Christ. From his birth to his ascension into heaven, angels played an essential role in the ministry of Christ. The fact that angels had an attentive role in the ministry of Jesus is another testimony of his deity. Just as they surround the throne of God the Father and serve him, they also were around Jesus—attending to God the Son.

Epilogue

From the Wilderness

A Summary of Jesus' Ministry!

After Jesus left the wilderness, he gathered a few of his disciples and headed back north to Capernaum for a few days before traveling to Cana for a wedding. Possibly his mother, Mary, was either related to the wedding party or was part of the wedding committee. This would mean Mary and her relatives would be embarrassed if they appeared inhospitable by running out of wine, giving Mary a reason to ask Jesus to intervene to turn water into wine for his first recorded miracle. At the same time, John the Baptist continued preaching the baptism of repentance for the forgiveness of sins. The whole Judean countryside and many of the people of Jerusalem went out to him. Confessing their sins, they were baptized by John in the Jordan River. Hundreds of people were now prepared for what was to come.

After the wedding, returning to Capernaum for a few days, Jesus headed down to Jerusalem to start the first part of his Judean ministry. After some time, Jesus returned to the Galilee region for his Galilean ministry in the power of the Spirit, and news about him spread throughout the region. He taught in their synagogues, and everyone praised him. Jesus went to Nazareth, where he had been brought up, and on one Sabbath day, he went into the synagogue, as was his custom. He stood up to read from the scroll of the prophet Isaiah that was handed to him. Unrolling it, he found the place where it is written: "The Spirit of the Lord is on me because he has anointed me to proclaim good news to the poor. He has sent me to proclaim freedom for the prisoners and recovery of sight for the blind, to set the oppressed free, to proclaim the year of the Lord's favor" (Isaiah 61:1-2).

Then he rolled up the scroll, returned it to the attendant, and sat down. The eyes of everyone in the synagogue were fastened on him. He began by saying to them, "Today, this scripture is fulfilled in your hearing."

All spoke well of him and were amazed at the gracious words that came from his lips. "Isn't this Joseph's son?" they asked. Jesus said to them, "Surely you will quote this proverb to me: 'Physician, heal yourself!' And you will tell me, 'Do here in your hometown what we have heard that you did in Capernaum.'"

"Truly I tell you," he continued, "no prophet is accepted in his hometown. I assure you that there were many widows in Israel in Elijah's time when the sky was shut for three and a half years, and there was a severe famine throughout the land. Yet Elijah was not sent to any of them but to a widow in Zarephath in the region of Sidon. And many in Israel had leprosy in the time of Elisha the prophet, yet not one was cleansed—only Naaman the Syrian."

All the people in the synagogue were furious when they heard this. They got up, drove him out of the town, and took him to the brow of the hill on which the town was built to throw him off the cliff. But he walked right through the crowd and went on his way. He returned to Capernaum, which is by the lake in the area of Zebulun and Naphtali, to make it the headquarters for his ministry.

Jesus traveled throughout the towns and villages of Galilee, preaching repentance, teaching about the Kingdom of God, and healing all who came to him.

Sometime later, Jesus returned to Jerusalem for Passover. Jewish leaders confronted Jesus about the healing on the Sabbath, which sparked threats to kill Jesus as they returned to the Galilee region.

By this time, Jesus heard that John had been imprisoned and withdrew to the Galilee area. People gathered along the mountainside, and Jesus preached to the multitude known as the *Sermon on the Mount*.

After building up his discipleship, he remained in the northern part of Galilee for some time because of the threat from the leaders, continuing with the teaching and healing of all who came to him. Many more recorded miracles were seen during this time as followers grew and traveled with Jesus. Jesus then returned to his hometown, Nazareth, for a second rejection.

By this time, Jesus started his third preaching tour throughout Galilee, and King Herod beheaded John the Baptist. Jesus and his disciples try to withdraw to a solitary place for rest, but the crowds followed them. This is where he feeds the five thousand.

After some time, Jesus traveled outside Galilee to Tyre through Sidon, and eventually he went to the Decapolis to feed the four thousand. He then sent the disciples two by two to preach on their own. After they returned, we see the feeding of the four thousand.

He then went back through the Sea of Galilee to Caesarea Philippi, where Peter confessed that Jesus was the Christ. After six days, Jesus took Peter, James, and John to a high mountain, and he was transfigured before them with a visit from Moses and Elijah.

When the Feast of Tabernacles was held in the autumn of AD 29, he returned to the Judean region for the remainder of his ministry, including returning to Bethany beyond the Jordan, where it all started, and then returned to Bethany and raised Lazarus from the dead.

Jesus ends his ministry with many more teachings at what is known as *"Holy Week,"* with a brutal death on the cross, a method of capital punishment in which the victim is tied or nailed to a large wooden cross or beam and left to hang until eventual death. Jesus did not deserve a death as severe as the one he got. But, because of his love for humanity, he willingly walked the two-and-a-half-mile road to Cavalry to receive all the world's sins while hanging to his death so he could open a doorway to heaven that otherwise would be hard to find.

Throughout his more than three years of ministry, Jesus healed many. His main itinerary was moving from one village to another, one side of the Jordan to the other, and one end of Canaan to another. By the end of his ministry, thirty-seven recorded miracles will be written within four gospels and taught throughout all of Galilee, Judea, and the world.

The End

I hope you enjoyed this imaginary journey of Jesus in the wilderness!
For a complete itinerary compiled from the gospels, see Appendix One, *60 Footsteps of Jesus.*

Afterword

Dear Reader,

Thank you for reading *The Itinerary*. As I wrote the manuscript, my thoughts were on you, the reader. I wanted to bring you a fictional story of Jesus' time in the wilderness without the reader, who might have a more mature and advanced relationship with our Savior, not being offended and crying out heresy.

Since there is no account of what took place with Jesus in the wilderness outside of temptations mentioned in the gospels. I wanted to stay within a biblical truth, as well as fill in the meaning behind the reason Jesus went into the wilderness. To pray, fast, spend time with his Father, and be filled with the Power of God to overcome the temptations of the enemy. The fact that while he was a man born of this world, he was also fully God. So, my focus was more on the man that still needed to learn the ways of his Father and, quite possibly, the full plan that had to be revealed to him.

As the thought of the story unfolded, I realized that there were not going to be too many characters needed to tell the story: Jesus, God, Lucifer, and angels. So, with some imagination, I added memories and the appearance of Joseph. The main characters whom the Bible already speaks are the main characters of the story. However, in the memories written about Jesus' family, only his brothers are mentioned in Mark 6:3 and Matthew 13:55. Therefore, I introduced into the story fictional names for his two sisters, Rebecca as the oldest sister and Martha as the younger sister, along with Rebecca's marriage to Asher, son of Eli, whom both are fictitious. Also, I fabricated the entire line of craftsmanship jobs mentioned in chapter five. The part when Jesus and Joseph went to Bethsaida to restore the boat for Zebedee, father to James and John, was to show that they already knew who Jesus was before he called them to go with him back to Galilee after the wilderness experience.

Scene One: Jesus's prayers, communication with God, homesickness for his family, and special visitor, are formatted from scriptures that are used as a backdrop. Scene Two: Disciples are revealed, Jesus and the Holy Spirit, and the itinerary is backed by scripture references. However, the conversation plot in both scenes is imaginary and means no disrespect to God, Jesus, or any Christian belief. Scene Three: Satan's temptations are used as a backdrop to expand conversations that are imaginary. Chapter thirteen-ministering Angel's visit is completely imaginary.

I pray that you enjoyed the story and learned something as well.

As a bonus, in the back of the book, I added a timeline of Jesus' life on earth, starting with his birth, to his ascension. This account has been correlated to the four gospels in Chronological order as best as I could determine.

As an appreciation, I wrote an expanded version of the conversation of the itinerary found in chapters 7, 8, and 9 as a full dialogue. If you would like a free copy, please visit, link.anthonyordille.com/TheItineraryHandout.

Blessings,

Anthony Ordille

Thank you for reading,
The Itinerary.

Gaining exposure as an independent author relies primarily on word-of-mouth, so if you have the time and inclination, please consider leaving a short-written candid review on Amazon or wherever you can.
Reviews do make a difference, and they also help others when considering the book.
Thank you!

Review Links:
link.anthonyordille.com/ReviewChannel

If you found this book helpful, please let others know where they can get a copy.

Sources and References

Since I was writing a Christian fiction about Jesus in the wilderness, it meant it now was going to be a historical work. I wanted to stay true to biblical accounts and first-century times, even though some of the dialogue may have a modern-day tone. The sources below represent the majority of the information that I incorporated into this novel.

I hereby acknowledge the following people and organizations for their contributions to this book as part of my research:

- The King James Bible
- The New King James Bible
- Biblegateway.com
- gotquestions.org (Got Questions Ministries)
- www.gotquestions.org/prayers-Jesus-prayed.html
- www.gotquestions.org/led-into-the-wilderness-to-be-tempted.html
- www.gotquestions.org/life-Peter.html
- www.gotquestions.org/John-the-Baptist-be-headed.html
- www.gotquestions.org/Simon-the-Zealot.html
- www.gotquestions.org/heavenly-crowns.html
- www.gotquestions.org/marriage-customs.html
- www.holylandsite.com/judean-wilderness
- www.givemechrist.com/2016/10/why-jesus-was-40-days-in-the-wilderness
- enduringword.com/bible-commentary/matthew-4
- en.wikipedia.org/wiki/Baptism_of_Jesus
- www.understandchristianity.com/teachings

- www.britannica.com/biography/Jesus/The-Jewish-religion-in-the-1st-century
- biblehub.com/weights-and-measures
- en.wikipedia.org/wiki/Biblical_mile
- jesus-messiah.com/html/passover-dates-26-34ad.html
- The 1999 movie "Jesus" with Jeremy Sisto
- Richard Bauckham's Living with Other Creatures: Green Exegesis and Theology (Baylor University Press, 2011).
- www.ccel.org/bible/phillips/JBPHarmony.htm, Story of Jesus Three Year Ministry Maps, Maps by Gordon Smith can be used without further permission.
- Second-century historian, Heqesippus, Apocalypse of James, & Ecclesiastical History, 1995, pp. 75-76.
- "Acts of Philip – especially Book 8". meta-religion.com. Retrieved 14 March 2007.
- The Biblical 40 Day fast by Vladimir Savchuk / January 10, 2022, pastorvlad.org/40dayfast (Used by Permission, 6/21/2023 by Everett Roeth).
- The Stages of Fasting: What Happens To Your Body When You Fast? Written by Dr. Group, DC., https://explore.globalhealing.com/stages-of-fasting-what-happens-when-you-fast/.

About the Author

Anthony Ordille was born in Hammonton, New Jersey, to a truck driver and a stay-at-home mom, with three brothers and two sisters. He attended Catholic school, then graduated from a public high school in 1976.

Anthony walked away from serving God as a teen, becoming rebellious and hateful. He lived a destructive life filled with alcohol, drugs, lying, cheating, stealing, adulterous acts, and rock 'n roll until he was thirty-two when he entered a rehab that introduced him to 12-step programs. At forty-one, he struggled with alcohol again until he surrendered his life to Jesus Christ on October 9, 1998.

Anthony wrote an autobiography, published in 2013. Since then, he has authored books on addiction and developed a Christ-centric Biblical 12-step program. Beyond addiction, Anthony has written several other helpful nonfiction and fiction books for Christian life, including one that would help Christians read the Bible in a year.

Upon returning to God, he completed the Associate Degree Program of Christian Studies (ACS) and Bachelor's Degree Program in Church Ministry (BCh.M). Anthony completed all his certifications to be a licensed minister from the Sure Foundation Theological Institute. On March 18, 2013, he was ordained in the Deacon Ministry with Gateway Church, Southlake, Texas. Anthony, a father of two with one adopted son, now resides in Dalzell, South Carolina, with his son, Jarred, and is actively involved at Christ Community Church.

He hopes his life experiences will inspire those struggling with addictions to find the truth and follow his lead to hope, peace, and forgiveness through his testimony and the program.

You can connect with Anthony through his website, www.anthonyordille.com, or link.anthonyordille.com/ConnectLandingPage.

Other Books by this Author

Please visit your favorite book retailer to discover other books by Anthony Ordille @ link.anthonyordille.com/Authorcentral or wherever books are sold.

Autobiography
An Injection of Faith: One Addict's Journey to Deliverance

Addiction
Overcome Addiction by God's Grace: 12-Steps to Freedom
Overcome Addiction by God's Grace: 12-Steps to Freedom Workbook
Breaking the Chains of Addiction: An Introduction to Addiction-Free Life
The 5 Essential Ways to Living Addiction-Free—Free Report

Christian Living
My Daily Scriptures: A Day by Day Bible Reading Guide— Here is a book that will help you read the Bible in a year, cover-to-cover, book-by-book.
My Daily Scriptures 365 Day Journal—Companion to guide book or as a standalone journal.

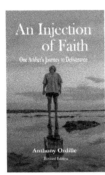

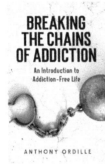

60 Footsteps of Jesus

Jesus' Early Years

#1) Jesus was born in Bethlehem as prophesied (Matthew 1:18-2:1).

It is believed that the year was 5 BC.

Angels herald his birth, and shepherds visit him (Luke 2:1-20).

Joseph and Mary presented him at the temple in Jerusalem according to Jewish law (Luke 2:21-40).

Magi from the East visited him within the first two years of his life (Matthew 2:1-12).

#2) Joseph, Mary, and Jesus fled to Egypt for safety from King Herod's plot to murder baby Jesus (Matthew 2:13-18).

#3) Joseph, Mary, and Jesus returned to Nazareth after they heard King Herod had died (4 BC) (Matthew 2:19-23).

Jesus grew up in Nazareth, visiting Jerusalem yearly for Passover (Luke 2:40-52).

*The Bible tells us nothing about what Jesus did between twelve and thirty. When Jesus was twelve, he went to Jerusalem with his family (Luke 2:41-52). After that, the next thing we hear about is his presence at a wedding in Cana (John 2:1-12). All the Bible tells us is that "Jesus grew in wisdom and stature, and in favor with God and man" (Luke 2:52). Therefore, we assume he lived with his parents and did what almost all children did back in his day: he worked with his father. His earthly father, Joseph, was a carpenter. That is why you will often see Jesus working as a carpenter in paintings.

I cannot tell you what happened with Jesus between twelve and thirty. We know he was perfectly obedient to his parents and did it for us to fulfill God's Law on our behalf. Then when he was thirty, he began to preach and teach and show his absolute power, which all pointed forward to his death for our sins three years later.

#4)-*Beginning of Ministry*

Jesus turned thirty in the autumn of AD 26, which was the biblical age that needed to be reached before a priest could begin to serve God (Numbers 4:3, 23, 47).

Jesus could have attended the *Feast of Dedication* before traveling from Jerusalem to the area John the Baptist was baptizing. This would place the baptism around the end of December or early January and line up with the scripture that says he went to Galilee, called Philip and Nathanael, and on the third day went to the wedding in Cana of Galilee (John 1:35-2:11).

The Bible is unclear on the time of year when the wedding occurred. However, the wedding is believed to occur in the spring or early summer because that was when most marriages were held in ancient Israel. Since scripture says he went to Jerusalem for Passover after the wedding, that would mean it was spring since Passover was held in April during that time frame.

#5)-John the Baptist's ministry of preparing people for the coming of the Messiah (Matthew 3:1-12; Mark 1:1-8; Luke 3:1-18; John 1:19-28).

John baptized Jesus in the Jordan River (winter AD 27) (Matthew 3:13-17; Mark 1:9-11; Luke 3:21-22; John 1:29-34).

*Bethany-beyond-the-Jordan is said to be the location of the baptism. It is in the Jordan Valley, east of the Jordan River, about five and a half miles north of the Dead Sea.

#6) Wilderness (Matthew 4:1-11; Mark 1:12-13; Luke 4:1-13).

THE ITINERARY · 141

*The Judean Wilderness runs from north of Jericho to the southern end of the Dead Sea. It lies on the western side of the lower Jordan Valley and the Dead Sea area. It is sixty miles long and about thirteen miles wide. It receives less than two inches of rain per year, so water is scarce and hard to find, and very little vegetation grows due to its lack of water and poor composition. The average daytime temperature would have been around 70-100 degrees Fahrenheit.

Because Mark 1:12-13 says immediately the Spirit drove him into the wilderness, we can assume that Jesus was in the northern part of the wilderness, though it is not recorded in scripture. Also, it appears Jesus returned to the area where he was baptized when he came out (John 1:29-43). It is also possible that Jesus walked along the western side of the Dead Sea and returned north to exit since he was there for forty days.

Early Judean Ministry

#7) Day 1-Jesus met Andrew, John, and Simon Peter (John 1:35-42).

#8) On Day 2-Left for Galilee (Bethsaida) and then found Philip, who told Nathanael (John 1:43-51).

#9) Day 3-He goes to Cana of Galilee for a wedding with his disciples and turned water into wine (John 2:1-11) (the first recorded miracle).

*When Jesus told his mother, "My hour has not come" (John 2:5), it could be because his official ministry had not started yet.

#10) Goes to Jerusalem for Passover (#1) (April AD 27) and cleared the money changers for the first time (John 2:13-25).

Nicodemus visited Jesus at night. Jesus taught him about the Kingdom of God (John 3:1-21).

The First Part of the Judean Ministry

#11) Spend time baptizing in the Judean countryside (John 3:22).

At Aemon near Salim, John the Baptist baptized and continued to point to Jesus as the Messiah (John 3:23-36).

#12) Passing through the territory of Samaria, near Sychar, Jesus met the Samaritan woman at the well. Many Samaritans believed in him (John 4:1-42).

#13) Returned to Cana of Galilee and healed a royal official's son who lay sick in Capernaum (John 4:43-54) (the second recorded miracle).

Galilean Ministry
#14) Jesus returned to Nazareth and preached in the synagogue but was rejected by the people in his hometown (Luke 4:14-30).

#15) Goes to Capernaum, which is by the lake in the area of Zebulun and Naphtali, and makes it his headquarters for ministry in Galilee (Matthew 4:12-17; Mark 1:14-15; Luke 4:31-32).

Jesus called Simon Peter, Andrew, James, and John as his disciples into full-time ministry along the Sea of Galilee (Matthew 4:18-22; Mark 1:16-20; Luke 5:1-22).

Also, in Capernaum, Jesus drove out an impure spirit from a man (Mark 1:21-28; Luke 4:33-37) (the third recorded miracle).

Jesus also healed Peter's mother-in-law from fever and many others (Mark 1:29-31; Luke 4:38-39) (the fourth recorded miracle).

Jesus healed many sick and oppressed in the evening (Mark 1:32-34; Luke 4:40-41) (the fifth recorded miracle).

**The calling in Luke 5:1-11 may be a later separate calling into full discipleship.

#16) Jesus traveled throughout the towns and villages of Galilee to preach and teach about the Kingdom of God (Matthew 4:23-25; Mark 1:35-39; Luke 4:42-44).

#17) First Miraculous catch of fish on the Lake of Gennesaret (Luke 5:1-11) (the sixth recorded miracle).

#18) In one of the towns, Jesus healed a man with leprosy (Matthew 8:2-4; Mark 1:40-45; Luke 5:12-16) (the seventh recorded miracle).

#19) Jesus returned to Capernaum and forgave and healed a paralyzed man lowered through the roof (Matthew 9:1-8; Mark 2:1-12; Luke 5:17-26) (the eighth recorded miracle).

Jesus called the tax collector Matthew into discipleship along the sea of Galilee (Matthew 9:9; Mark 2:13-14; Luke 5:27-28).

While having dinner at Matthew's house, Jesus taught the Pharisees about God's mercy (Matthew 9:10-13; Mark 23:15-17; Luke 5:29-32).

Jesus is questioned about fasting and taught about the new covenant with a parable (Matthew 9:14-17; Mark 2:18-22; Luke 5:33-39).

On two separate Sabbaths, Jesus defends himself as Lord of the Sabbath (Matthew 12:1-14; Mark 2:23-36; Luke 6:1-11).

#20) Sometime later, Jesus returned to Jerusalem for a Jewish feast (Passover #2) (April AD 28). He healed a man near a pool (John 5:1-9) (the ninth recorded miracle).

Jewish leaders confronted Jesus about healing on the Sabbath. He taught them about his authority and the scriptures that testify about him (John 5:31-47).

#21) Returning north to Galilee, Jesus healed the man with the shriveled hand (Matthew 12:9; Mark 3:1; Luke 6:6) (the tenth recorded miracle). It is around this time that John the Baptist is imprisoned.

#22) Returned to the Galilee area. He went up to the mountainside with his disciples and chose twelve of them to be his apostles (Mark 3:13-19; Luke 6:12-16).

Finding a level place along the mountainside, Jesus delivered his famous *Sermon on the Mount* to the crowds teaching about prayer, justice, care for the needy, handling the religious law, divorce, fasting, judging others, salvation, and much more. Otherwise known as Beatitudes (Matthew 5:1-7:29; Luke 6:17-49).

**The exact location of the Sermon on the Mount is not given in scripture. A mountainside between Capernaum and Gennesaret has historically been the most recognized possibility.

#23) Returned to Capernaum, where he healed a centurion's servant (Matthew 8:5-13; Luke 7:1-10) (the eleventh recorded miracle).

#24) Jesus traveled to Nain, where he raised a widow's son back to life (Luke 7:11-17) (the twelfth recorded miracle).

Perhaps in or around Nain, John the Baptist's disciples came to him with a question about who Jesus was (Matthew 11:2-19; Luke 7:18-35).

Even after seeing his miracles, Jesus denounces the towns that failed to repent (Matthew 11:20-30).

Jesus is invited to dinner at a Pharisee's house, where he is anointed with oil by a sinful woman (Luke 7:36-50).

#25) Jesus again traveled and preached throughout Galilee (Luke 8:1-3).

During this preaching and teaching tour, Jesus is accused of being demon-possessed, confronted by his family, and demanded a miraculous sign (Matthew 12:22-50; Mark 3:20-35, Luke 8:19-21). He also taught the people using many parables (Matthew 13:1-53; Mark 4:1-34; Luke 8:4-18).

#26) While crossing the Sea of Galilee, Jesus calmed a storm threatening to drown him and his disciples (Matthew 8:18, 23-27; Mark 4:35-41; Luke 8:22-25) (the thirteenth recorded miracle).

#27) In the Gerasenes (or Gadarenes) area, Jesus restored a demon-possessed man by casting out demons into a herd of swine (Matthew 8:28-34; Mark 5:1-20; Luke 8:26-39) (the fourteenth recorded miracle).

**(This could have taken place near the town of Gadara or near the town of Gerasa.)

#28) Most likely, returned to Capernaum, a large crowd meets Jesus. He performs the trio miracles: Life of the Dead, Sight to the Blind, and Speech to the Dumb. He healed a woman subject to bleeding for twelve years (the fifteenth recorded miracle). Then he raised a synagogue leader (Jairus's) daughter back to life (Matthew 9:18-26; Mark 5:21-43; Luke 8:40-56) (the sixteenth recorded miracle).

Jesus healed two blind men and then cast a demon out of a mute man (Matthew 9:27-34) (the seventeenth and eighteenth recorded miracle).

#29) Jesus went to his hometown of Nazareth and was again rejected (Matthew 13:54-58; Mark 6:1-6).

#30) Jesus conducted a third preaching tour throughout Galilee. He also sent out his twelve disciples two-by-two to preach the gospel, giving them the power to heal diseases and drive out demons (Matthew 9:35-11:1; Mark 6:6-13; Luke 9:1-6).

It is during this time that King Herod beheads John the Baptist (Matthew 14:1-12; Mark 6:14-29; Luke 9:7-9).

#31) After his disciples returned, Jesus took them across the Sea of Galilee to Bethsaida. He and his disciples try to withdraw to a solitary place for rest, but the crowds follow them. When it got late, Jesus had compassion on them and miraculously fed them using five loaves of bread and two fishes. The number of people who ate was 5,000 men, besides women and children (Matthew 14:13-21; Mark 6:3-44; Luke 9:10-17; John 6:1-13) (the nineteenth recorded miracle).

Jesus sent his disciples ahead of him while he went to a mountainside to pray at night. They got in a boat and traveled across the lake (Matthew 14:22-23; Mark 6:45-46; John 6:14-15).

*This appeared to be around the third Passover (#3) (April AD 29) that Jesus did not attend because of the plot to kill him (John 6:4).

#32) While his disciples were straining against the rough waters, Jesus met them in the middle of the lake by walking on water (Matthew 14:24-33; Mark 6:47-52; John 6:16-21) (the twentieth recorded miracle).

#33) Jesus and his disciples landed in Gennesaret, and he healed many people (Matthew 14:34-36; Mark 6:53-56) (the twenty-first recorded miracle).

#34) The people found Jesus in Capernaum. He taught them about faith and that he was the Bread of Life. Many of his followers abandoned him because they did not like what they heard (John 6:22-71).

Possibly in Capernaum, Jesus confronted the Pharisees about their anti-scriptural traditions (Matthew 15:1-20; Mark 7:1-23; John 7:1).

#35) Jesus traveled outside of Israel to the region of Tyre, where he healed the young daughter of a Syrophoenician woman (Matthew 15:21-28; Mark 7:24-30) (the twenty-second recorded miracle).

#36) Jesus traveled through Sidon, down to the Sea of Galilee, and eventually to the Decapolis. In this region, people brought lame, blind, crippled, mute, and many more whom he all healed, including a man who was deaf and mute (the twenty-third recorded miracle). He also miraculously fed the crowd, which included 4,000 men, besides women and children (Matthew 15:29-15:38; Mark 7:31-8:9) (the twenty-fourth recorded miracle).

#37) After crossing the lake, Jesus came to Magadan (or Dalmanutha), where he rebuked Pharisees who demanded a miraculous sign (Matthew 15:39-16:4; Mark 8:10-12).

#38) As Jesus and his disciples cross the lake again, he warned them of *The Leaven of the Pharisees and Sadducees* (Matthew 16:5-12; Mark 8:13-21).

Upon reaching Bethsaida, Jesus healed a blind man (Mark 8:22-26) (the twenty-fifth recorded miracle).

#39) Jesus and his disciples traveled to Caesarea Philippi. Peter confessed that Jesus was the Christ, and Jesus promised that the gates of Hades would not overcome Christ's Church. Jesus also gave the "key to the Kingdom of Heaven" (Matthew 16:13-20; Mark 8:27-30; Luke 9:18-21).

Jesus taught his disciples that he would suffer, be killed, and be raised to life again after three days. He also taught them that all followers of Christ must be willing to carry their "cross" and follow him (Matthew 16:21-28; Mark 8:31-9:1; Luke 9:22-27).

#40) After six days, Jesus took three of his disciples (Peter, James, and John) to a high mountain, and he was transfigured before them. Old Testament believers Moses and Elijah also appear with Jesus. Jesus told his disciples not to tell anyone about this transfiguration until after his resurrection (Matthew 17:1-13; Mark 9:2-13; Luke 9:28-36).

*The traditional location of the Mount of Transfiguration is Mount Tabor, about eleven miles west of the Sea of Galilee. However, it has been suggested that Mount Hermon is the site of Jesus' transfiguration due to its height and proximity to Caesarea Philippi. Ultimately, no one knows on which mountain this event took place.

Upon descending the mountain, Jesus cast a demon out of a boy and healed him (Matthew 17:14-20; Mark 9:14-28; Luke 9:37-42) (the twenty-sixth recorded miracle).

#41) Returning to Galilee, Jesus again foretells his death and resurrection for a second time (Matthew 17:22-23; Mark 9:30-32; Luke 9:43-45).

In Capernaum, Jesus used the paying of the temple tax to teach that he is the Son of God. (Matthew 17:24-27) (the twenty-seventh recorded miracle).

He also taught his disciples that childlike faith and a willingness to be a servant to all make a person the "greatest in the Kingdom of Heaven" (Matthew 18:1-5; Mark 9:33-37; Luke 9:46-50).

He also spent this time teaching about not causing others to sin (Matthew 18:6-11; Mark 9:42-50), rewards in the Kingdom of Heaven (Mark 9:38-41), confronting sin in fellow believers and leading them toward repentance (Matthew 18:12-35), and the cost of following him (Matthew 8:18-22; Luke 9:57-62).

He also confronted the unbelief of his brothers (John 7:2-9).

Later Judean Ministry

#42) Now, the Jews' *Feast of Tabernacles* was at hand. His brothers wanted him to go into Judea so that his disciples also may see the works that he was doing. Then Jesus said to them, "My time has not yet come, but your time is always ready. The world cannot hate you but hates me because I testify that its works are evil. You go up to this feast. I am not yet attending this feast, for my time has not yet fully come." When he had said these things to them, he remained in Galilee (John 7:2-9).

Jesus secretly set out for Jerusalem to attend the *Feast of Tabernacles* (autumn of AD 29). He decided to pass through Samaria, but the people of some Samaritan villages did not welcome him. When his disciples reacted angrily, Jesus rebuked them, and they traveled to another village (Luke 9:51-56; John 7:10).

While the Jewish leaders were looking for Jesus at the *Feast of Tabernacles*, the people whispered and debated about Jesus (John 7:11-13).

Halfway through the festival, Jesus appeared in the temple courts and taught the people. While he teaches them, the Jewish leaders bring to him a woman caught in adultery to test him. He then taught about who he is; The Jewish leaders disputed Jesus' claims. After referring to himself with the divine name of the Lord, "I AM" (John 8:58), the unbelieving Jews attempted to stone him, but he slipped away (John 7:14-8:59).

Jesus healed a man born blind (the twenty-eighth recorded miracle), and the Pharisees investigated the healing. Jesus taught the Pharisees that he is the gate and the Good Shepherd (John 9:1-10:21).

#43) Jesus sent out the seventy people to spread the gospel message in every town and village where he was about to go. They returned to him with joy in their successful work (Luke 10:1-24).

He also spent this time teaching the Parable of the Good Samaritan (Luke 10:25-37), teaching in Mary and Martha's house in Bethany (Luke 10:38-42), teaching about prayer (Luke 11:1-13), teaching about asking for a sign (Luke 11:14-36), warning about religious hypocrisy (Luke 11:37-54), and warning against the teaching of the Pharisees, against worry, and about being ready (Luke 12:1-13:9).

- Warning and Encouragement (Luke 12:1-12).
- Parable of the Rich Fool (Luke 12:13-21).
- Do not Worry (Luke 12:22-34).
- The Faithful Servant and Evil Servant (Luke 12:35-48).
- Christ Brings Division (Luke 12:49-59).
- Discern the Time (Luke 12:54-59).
- Repent or Perish (Luke 13:1-9).

- As he was teaching, he was casting out a demon that was mute (Luke 11:14) (the twenty-ninth recorded miracle).
- He also healed a disabled woman and used it to teach about the Sabbath and the Kingdom of God (Luke 13:10-21) (the thirtieth recorded miracle).

#44) Celebrating the *Festival of Dedication in Jerusalem* (December AD 29). Jesus once again taught in the temple courts and confronted the unbelief of his Jewish opponents (John 10:22-39).

#45) Jesus returned to Bethany beyond the Jordan (Perea), where his ministry started and taught in the region John the Baptist had been baptizing over two and a half years earlier (John 10:40-42).

Jesus taught the people of this region about entering the Kingdom of God (Luke 13:22-30), his impending death in Jerusalem (Luke 13:31-35), compassion and humility (Luke 14:1-14), not rejecting the invitation to eternal life (Luke 14:15-24), willingness to put God above anyone and anything (Luke 14:25-35), compassion for the lost (Luke 15:1-32), focusing on God and God's Word (Luke 16:1-31), and the importance of forgiveness and a faith-filled attitude of service to God (Luke 17:1-10).

During this time, when he went into the house of one of the rulers of the Pharisees to eat bread on the Sabbath, they watched him closely. And behold, there was a certain man before him who had dropsy. And Jesus, answering, spoke to the lawyers and Pharisees, saying, "Is it lawful to heal on the Sabbath?" But they kept silent. And he took him and healed him and let him go (Luke 14:1-4) (the thirty-first recorded miracle).

#46) Not long before his death on the cross, Jesus heard that his friend, Lazarus, had died in Bethany. Jesus raised Lazarus from the dead (John 11:38-44) (the thirty-second recorded miracle), creating a commotion in Jerusalem and the surrounding areas. Because of this, some Pharisees who did not believe in Jesus planned to have him killed (John 11:45-52).

#47) Hearing of the Pharisees' plot to kill him, Jesus withdrew to a village called Ephraim with his disciples (John 11:53-57).

It seems that from here, Jesus traveled northward to meet up with Jewish pilgrims going from Galilee to Jerusalem for the festival of the Passover.

*The location of Ephraim is not known with certainty but has been said to be the modern-day town of Taibe (Taiyibah or Taiyibeh).

#48) Possibly in the southern part of Galilee bordering Samaria, Jesus joined the pilgrims traveling to Jerusalem for the Passover. While traveling, Jesus healed ten lepers (the thirty-third recorded miracle), taught about the "Last Days," and told two parables to encourage his disciples to pray (Luke 17:11-18:14).

#49) Going on from Galilee with the crowd and back through Perea, east side of the Jordan River flat land, Jesus taught the crowds about divorce (Matthew 19:1-12; Mark 10: 1-12), the importance of the Kingdom of God for little children (Matthew 19:13-15; Mark 10:13-16; Luke 18:15-17), recognizing that one is saved by God's seemingly impossible grace in Jesus and not by works (Matthew 19:16-30; Mark 10:17-31; Luke 18:18-30) and that this grace is given to all equally (Matthew 20:1-16).

Jesus also predicted for the third time his suffering and death coming up in Jerusalem, which showed the disciples the proper attitude of being a servant for others (Matthew 20:17-28; Mark 10:32-45; Luke 18:31-34; John 12:27-36) (John has it in after Triumphal Entrance).

#50) Jesus and his disciples traveled to Jericho on their way to Jerusalem. While in Jericho, Jesus healed two blind men (Matthew 20:29-34; Mark 10:46-52; Luke 18:35-43) (the thirty-fourth recorded miracle), brought a chief tax collector named Zacchaeus to repentance (Luke 19:1-10), and taught about using the talents God gives for this kingdom (Luke 19:11-27).

From here, Jesus headed to Jerusalem for the final week before his death (Luke 19:28).

Holy Week

#51) Jesus arrived in the Jerusalem area for the last week of his earthly ministry, called the Holy Week festival of the Passover (#4) (April AD 30).

#52) The day before Palm Sunday, the Sabbath, reaching Bethany, the home of Lazarus, Martha, and Mary, Jesus had dinner and was anointed by Mary (John 12:1-8).

Sunday morning, Jesus sent two disciples for the colt (Matthew 21:1-6; Mark 11:1-7; Luke 19: 29-35).

They traveled back and forth from the Mount of Olives to the temple each day.

#53) The Events of Holy Week

Palm Sunday - Afternoon Triumphal Entry (Matthew 21:7-11; Mark 11:1-11; Luke 19:36-44; John 12:12-19).

Monday—Cursing of the fig tree on the way into Jerusalem (Matthew 21:18-19; Mark 11:12-14) (the thirty-fifth recorded miracle).

- Cleansing of the Temple a second time (Matthew 21:12-13; Mark 11:15-19; Luke 19:45-46). (Matthew's account has this on Sunday).
- Healed the blind and the lame at the temple (Matthew 21:14-17).

The Gospel of John has these right after his triumphal entrance, but most likely, since it was late in the day they are meant for Monday.

- The Fruitful Grain of Wheat (John 12:20-26).
- Jesus Predicts His Death on the Cross (John 12:27-36).

- Who Has Believed Our Report? (John 12:37-41).
- Walk in the Light (John 12:42-50).

Tuesday—Was a hectic teaching day.
- The majority of the day, answering questions from the Pharisees, Sadducees, chief priests, and leaders (Matthew 21:23-22:1-46).
- Lesson of the Withered Fig Tree (Matthew 21:20-22; Mark 11:20-26).
- Challenge of Jesus' Authority (Matthew 21:23-27; Mark 11:27-33; Luke 20:1-8).
- Parables of Warning (Matthew 21:28-22:14; Mark 12:1-12; Luke 20:9-19).
- Debate with Jewish Leaders (Matthew 22:15-46; Mark 12:13-37; Luke 20:20-44).
- Denunciation of the Scribes and Pharisees (Matthew 23:1-39; Mark 12:38-44; Luke 20:45-21:4).

Headed back to Mount of Olives (Speaks on End Times).
Discourse on the Last Things (Matthew 24-25; Mark 13; Luke 21:5-38).
- Jesus predicts the Destruction of the Temple (Matthew 24:1-2; Mark 13:1-2; Luke 21:5-6).
- The Signs of the Times and the End of the Age (Matthew 24:3-14; Mark 13:3-13; Luke 21:7-24).
- The Great Tribulation (Matthew 24:15-28; Mark 13:14-23).
- The Coming of the Son of Man (Matthew 24:29-31; Mark 13:24-27; Luke 21:25-28).
- The Parable of the Fig Tree (Matthew 24:32-35; Mark 13:28-31; Luke 21:29-33).
- No One Knows the Day or Hour (Matthew 24:36-44; Mark 13:32-37; Luke 21:34-38).
- The Faithful Servant and the Evil Servant (Matthew 24:45-51).

- The Parable of the Wise and Foolish Virgins (Matthew 25:1-13).
- The Parable of the Talents (Matthew 25:14-30).
- The Son of Man Will Judge the Nations (Matthew 25:31-46).

Wednesday—It seemed to be a quiet day.
- Conspiracy of the Chief Priests (Matthew 26:1-5; Mark 14:1-2; Luke 22:1-2).
- Second anointing of Jesus by an unnamed woman in Bethany at Simon the leper's house (Matthew 26:6-13; Mark 14:3-9).
- The plot of Judas Iscariot sealed the deal to betray Jesus (Matthew 26:14-16; Mark 14:10-11; Luke 22:3-6.

Maundy Thursday—The day of unleavened bread.
- Sent Peter and John to make preparations (Luke 22:8-13).
- The Last Supper (Matthew 26:17-35;Mark 14:12-31; Luke 22:7-38; John 13-17).
  - Communion (Matthew 26:26-30; Mark 14:22-26; Luke 22:14-23).
  - The disciples argue about greatness (Luke 22:24-30).
  - Jesus washes the disciple's feet (John 13:1-17).
  - Jesus identifies his betrayer (John 13:18-30).
  - Jesus predicts Peter's betrayal (Matthew 26:31-35; Mark 14:27-31; Luke 22:31-34; John 13:36-38).
- Jesus comforted his disciples (John 13:31-35, 14:1-24; 15:1-27).
  - The New Commandment (John 13:31-35).
  - The Way, the Truth, and the Life (John 14:1-6).
  - The Father Revealed (John 14:7-11).
  - The Answered Prayer (John 14:12-14).
  - Jesus Promises Another Helper (John 14:15-18).

- The Indwelling of the Father and the Son (John 14:19-24).
  - Jesus Promises the Holy Spirit (John 14:25-31).
  - Supplies for the Road (Luke 22:35-38).
- Goes to Gethsemane (Matthew 26:36-46; Mark 14:32-42; Luke 22:39-46).
- Jesus spoke to the disciples along the way with some last-minute teachings.
  - The True Vine (John 15:1-8).
  - Love and Joy Perfected (John 15:9-17).
  - The World's Hatred (John 15:18-25).
  - The Coming Rejection (John15: 26-27).
  - Jesus Warns and Comforts His Disciples (John 16:1-4).
  - The Work of the Holy Spirit (John 16:5-15).
  - Sorrow Will Turn to Joy (John 16:16-24).
  - Jesus Christ Has Overcome the World (John 16: 25-33).
  - Jesus prayed for himself, his disciples, and all believers when they arrived (John 17:1-26).
- Betrayal and Arrest (Matthew 26:47-56; Mark 14:43-52; Luke 22:47-53; John 18:1-11) Restored, Malchus, high priests' servant's ear (Luke 22:49-51, John 18:10) (the thirty-sixth recorded miracle).
- The trial before the Jewish Authorities (Matthew 26:57-68; Mark 14:53-65; Luke 22:63-71; John 18:12-14).
- Peter disowned Jesus (Matthew 26:69-75; Mark 14:66-72; Luke 22:54-62; John 18:15-18, 25-27).
- Jesus was mocked and beaten (Matthew 27: 27-31; Mark 15:16-20; Luke 22:63-65; John 19:1-4).

Good Friday—Trial before Pilate and Herod (Matthew 27:1-26; Mark 15:1-15; Luke 23:1-25; John 18:19-24, 28-40, 19:5-16).

- Judas hung himself (Matthew 27:3-10).

- Crucifixion (Matthew 27:32-56; Mark 15:21-41; Luke 23:26-49; John 19:17-37).
- Burial in Joseph's tomb (Matthew 27:57-61; Mark 15:42-47; Luke 23:50-56; John 19:38-42).

Saturday - Watch at the Tomb (Matthew 27:62-66).

Easter Sunday—The Resurrection (Matthew 28:1-10; Mark 16:1-8; Luke 24:1-12; John 20:1-18).

- The Guards Report (Matthew 28:11-15).

Post-Resurrection

#54) Three days after being crucified for the sins of the world, Jesus was raised from the dead. On that Sunday, he appeared to many people.

- There was a great earthquake, not to let Jesus out of the tomb but to permit witnesses to enter (Matthew 28:2-4).
- Mary Magdalene, Mary, the mother of James, Salome, Joanna, and other women, come to the tomb at daybreak, leaving their homes while it was still dark (Matthew 28:1; Mark 16:1-4; Luke 24:1; John 20:1).
- Mary Magdalene ran to tell Peter and John (John 20:2).
- The other women entered the tomb and were addressed by the angel (Matthew 28:5-8; Mark 16:2-8; Luke 24:2-7).
- Peter and John arrived at the tomb after the women had left (Luke 24:12; John 20:3-10).
- Jesus appeared to Mary Magdalene (Mark 16:9-11; John 20:11-17) "First one to see him."
- Jesus appeared to the other women (Matthew 28:9-10).
- The chief priests and the elders bribe the guards to cover up the resurrection (Matthew 28:11-15).

- The women told the disciples (Luke 24:8-11; John 20:18).
- Jesus appeared to Peter (Luke 24:34; 1 Corinthians 15:5).
- Jesus appeared to the Emmaus disciples (Mark 16:12-13; Luke 24:13-35).

#55) The order of this event and the previous event could be interchanged.
- Jesus appeared to the ten in the upper room (1st appearance) (Luke 24:36-43; John 20:19-23).
- Jesus appeared to Thomas (John 20:24-25).

#56) Jesus, one week later, appeared to all disciples (2nd appearance) (John 20:26-31).

#57) Jesus appeared to seven disciples at the sea of Galilee (3rd appearance) (John 21:1-25).
- Peter, Thomas, Nathanael, James, John, and two more disciples went fishing. They caught nothing. Jesus called out to them from the shore to drop their nets (the second miraculous catch of fish) (the thirty-seventh recorded miracle).
- Jesus restored Peter (John 21:15-19).

He later met eleven of his disciples on a mountain in Galilee and gave them the Great Commission (Matthew 28:16-20) (Matthew is the only gospel that says Great Commission was in Galilee).

*It is possible that Jesus appeared to 500 believers also occurred at this time (1 Corinthians 15:6).

#58) Jesus appeared to his brother James.

*Maybe to reveal to James that he was the Messiah so James and the rest of his brothers and sisters would believe and tell him all about the ministry he will have (1 Corinthians 15:7).

#59) Jesus led, or met, his disciples to the vicinity of Bethany. Mount of Olives. There he blessed them (The

Great Commission) (Mark 16:14-18; Luke 24:44-49; Acts 1: 1-8).

#60) Ascension (Mark 16:19-20; Luke 24:50-53; Acts 1:9-11).

- The upper room prayer meeting was on the same day as Ascension (Acts 1:12-26).
- This was ten days before the event on Pentecost, which is seen in Acts 2:1-47.

As an afterthought, this is not the end of the story. The disciples and apostles performed miracles, just as Jesus had performed miracles, for years until their death. Many of those same miracles occur throughout the world today in various churches.

Note:

Even though not mentioned in scripture, Jesus could have gone to Jerusalem for the *"Feast of Tabernacles"* and *"Feast of Dedication"* during the ministry since this would have been the custom Autumn/Winter AD 27 and AD 28).

If you would like a free pdf copy to use in meetings or bible studies, visit link.anthonyordille.com/60footstepsofjesus.

Appendix Two

Fasting Guide

Four elements will evolve outside of the natural
fast from a spiritual fast.

1. It is a preparation for ministry.

No matter how long someone has been in ministry or if
they are starting, fasting is essential to hear from God the
direction the ministry is to take. By reading scripture, we can
see that Jesus did not begin his ministry before fasting, nor
are there any recordings of him preaching or being used by
the Holy Spirit before this fast. The only account is in Luke
2:42-51 when his parents went to Jerusalem for the feast of
the Passover like they did every year. "*And when he was twelve,
they went up to Jerusalem according to the custom of the feast. When
they had finished the days, the boy Jesus lingered behind in Jerusalem
as they returned.*"

The lingering in the temple was neither mischievous nor
disobedient but a natural result of his knowledge that he
must be about his Father's business. That he was astonish-
ing to the temple teachers with his wisdom and knowledge
speaks to his extraordinary abilities. At the same time, his
listening and asking questions of his elders shows that he
was utterly respectful, taking the role of a student as was
fitting for a child of his age.

Beyond that, we all know that "Jesus grew in wisdom and
stature and favor with God and men" (Luke 2:52).

This is why the Spirit of God led him into the wilderness
to prepare him for ministry. We can see that after the forty
days, scripture makes it a point to mention that Jesus returns
from his fast in power. "*Then Jesus returned in the power of the*

Spirit to Galilee, and news of him went out through all the surrounding regions" (Luke 4:14).

2. It Provokes a Cleansing.

In the Bible, only three essential men were led to do an extended forty-day fast—Moses, Elijah, and Jesus. The concept of fasting for forty days comes from the example we see in the Bible.

The number (40) generally symbolizes a testing, trial, or probation period. But it can also mean a time of cleansing, as we see in Genesis 6:8. *"For forty days and nights, God flooded the earth and 'cleansed it of evil,' leaving only Noah and his family alive because they had found favor in the eyes of the Lord."*

In these extended fasts, our spirit is hypersensitive to what is pleasing to God, and as a result, he can do a much deeper cleanse within our hearts.

3. It has to be led by the Holy Spirit.

In scripture, the Lord led Moses to do a forty-day fast.

"So, he was there with the Lord forty days and forty nights; he neither ate bread nor drank water. And he wrote on the tablets the words of the covenant, the Ten Commandments" (Exodus 34:28).

Elijah was also given a specific direction before fasting for forty days and nights.

"And the angel of the Lord came back the second time, and touched him, and said, "Arise and eat, because the journey is too great for you. So he arose, and ate and drank; and he went in the strength of that food forty days and forty nights as far as Horeb, the mountain of God" (1 Kings 19:7,8).

And we already saw in the gospels that the Spirit led Jesus into the wilderness.

When we do a fast of this length, we should allow God to lead us to its length and strain on the body. It can be hazardous to your health if not directed by God.

4. Expect a Spiritual Battle.

When Jesus fasted for forty days, we see in scripture that he faced opposition from Satan. Satan attacked his mind and emotions. This is the only place where Satan can attack us, so we must be prepared. If God leads us to do this fast, our body will be able to handle it, but the difficulty will be conquering the battle in the mind.

This is why we need to prepare our minds and our soul before our fast for whatever emotions may come. We may experience discouragement, cravings, or a strong desire to give up.

Remember, his grace will lighten the burden when God leads us to fast. We are to be encouraged by faith for the outcome and that a fast is not for us to accomplish a goal but for God to accomplish his purpose in us.[185]

Disclosure:

†Results may vary. The information and statements are for educational purposes and are not intended to replace your doctor's advice. See your physician if you have a severe medical condition or health concern.

---

[185] The Biblical 40 Day fast by Vladimir Savchuk, January 10, 2022, pastorvlad.org/40dayfast.

Printed in the USA
CPSIA information can be obtained
at www.ICGtesting.com
LVHW021453070124
768338LV00003B/307

9 798987 800478